&

Flowers in the Shade

During the Rains

&

Flowers in the Shade

TWO NOVELLAS BY NAGAI KAFU

TRANSLATED BY LANE DUNLOP

STANFORD UNIVERSITY PRESS

STANFORD, CALIFORNIA

1994

Stanford University Press
Stanford, California
© 1994 by the Board of Trustees
of the Leland Stanford Junior University
Printed in the United States of America

During the Rains was originally published in
Japanese in 1931 under the title TSUYU NO ATOSAKI;
Flowers in the Shade was originally published in
Japanese in 1934 under the title HIKAGE NO HANA.

Kafu Nagai TSUYU NO ATOSAKI / HIKAGE NO HANA
© 1931 and 1934 Hisamitsu Nagai
Originally published in Japan

The Translator's Preface and notes were prepared
especially for this edition by Lane Dunlop.

CIP data appear at the end of the book

Stanford University Press publications are distributed exclusively by Stanford University Press within
the United States, Canada, and Mexico; they are
distributed exclusively by Cambridge University
Press throughout the rest of the world.

To Edward G. Seidensticker

In general admiration of his work
and in particular admiration of
Kafu the Scribbler
which introduced me to this author

CONTENTS

NAGAI KAFU was born on December 3, 1879, in the
Koishikawa district of Tokyo. His father, Hisaichiro, was
an important Meiji-era bureaucrat; his mother, Tsune,
was the daughter of a well-known Confucian scholar.
The two had met and married when Hisaichiro was a
student of Tsune's father.

At that time Koishikawa was in the country, an area
of old estates and temples. It took its name from the
brook (literally, the name means "pebble river") that still
flowed above ground in Kafu's childhood. One of Kafu's
early stories, "The Fox," is about a fox discovered to be
living on the grounds of the family house that is ruthlessly
smoked out and killed by Kafu's father and his staunch
henchman, the student-houseboy. The eventual disap-
pearance of his childhood scenes under the pavements of
the city in its ineluctable expansion must have gone far to
shape Kafu's sensibility. In much of his mature work, he
is forever lamenting the passage of the good old days and
their replacement by the bad new days.

A reluctant student who kept playing hooky to attend
kabuki performances rather than university lectures, take
shakuhachi flute lessons in the Yanagibashi geisha district,
apprentice himself to the Edo-style playwright Fukuchi
Ochi, and occasionally appear on the boards himself, Kafu
steeped himself in Edo period literature and also read such
foreign authors as Zola and Maupassant in English and
then French. His early works include *Ambition* (1902), *The*

Flowers of Hell (1902), and *The Woman of the Dream* (1903). *Ambition*, the story of the rise and fall of a young Meiji businessman misled by newly imported precepts of success, is written in Kafu's peculiar variety of Naturalism, in which personal taste and evocation replace the dispassionate zeal and scientific reportage of Zola. *Flowers of Hell* provides an early forerunner of Tsuruko, the writer Kiyooka's wife in *During the Rains*, a woman educated beyond the needs of her society. *The Woman of the Dream* details a woman's descent into degradation and the absence of judgment that we find in the later *Flowers in the Shade*.

These early works, written before Kafu's departure in September 1903 for America and later France, although demonstrating that Kafu was *sui generis*, a writer who could not be fitted into the framework of the Naturalism and "pure literature" that dominated the Japanese literary world of the time, are not among his major works. It was his literary activity in the years following his return to Japan in August 1908 that revealed his characteristic terrain as a writer.

Kafu had been dispatched abroad by his father as a means of concealing his unsatisfactory progress along the road to conventional success and to accustom him to the discipline required for that success. To this end, Kafu worked at Japanese banks in America and France, in addition to engaging in more student-like pursuits. From his travels came *Tales of America* (1908) and *Tales of France* (1909). Most of the stories in the former are based on accounts of life in America that Kafu heard from Japanese immigrants; in the latter, hardly any Japanese appear, aside from Kafu himself in various personae. Nakamura Mitsuo, a Japanese critic, has remarked that Kafu acquired his belief in individualism from his stay in America and his belief in traditionalism in France, where, having already been exposed to it in America, he was able to ignore the mechanical aspect of Western civilization. These beliefs were to stand Kafu in good stead when he returned to Japan, where individualism as such was not acknowledged until after the Pacific War and where until well after the Meiji era (1868–1912) civilization was equated with modernization. It is interesting to reflect that Kafu, the bulk of whose work is properly thought of as quintessentially Japanese in its evocation of the passing scenes and seasons of Tokyo, the city that found its chronicler in him, may at the outset of his career have undergone a definitive molding of his sensibility in America. The thoroughgoing individualism and natural beauty of America influenced Kafu, both in his eccentric social stance and in the sensitivity to nature evidenced in his work, long after they had disappeared as subject matter from his stories. Kafu's American-inspired individualism, among other things, may have enabled him to hold out unmoved against the patriotic hysteria of the war years.

It is with "The Fox" (1909) that Kafu's most characteristic work, with its nostalgic tone, may be said to begin. It is the first of his stories published after his return to Japan to use Japanese materials. Although short, and more of a childhood memory piece than a story, it is rightly counted among his masterpieces.

There followed a series of evocations of the vanishing past, its pleasures, pursuits, and professions: "The River Sumida" (1909), *Sneers* (1909–10), *The Kept Woman's House* (1912), *Geisha in Rivalry* (1917), *Dwarf Bamboo* (1920), and *Quiet Rain* (1921). Perhaps the most typical of these, as well as the most masterly, is *Geisha in Rivalry*. Drawing on his experiences in the Shinbashi geisha district, Kafu depicts in detail the life of the geishas and their fashionable gentlemen customers, the former sympathetically, the latter critically and with a certain measure of contempt. After a decade-long hiatus, which has been attributed to Kafu's distaste for the brave new Japan, there appeared *During the Rains* (1931) and *Flowers in the Shade* (1934), his chronicles of life in the Tokyo "floating world" of the late 1920's and early 1930's. *A Strange Tale from East of the River* (1937), Kafu's account of his summer evening visits to a lady of the night in the Tamanoi quarter, is perhaps the most intense distillation of his longing for the past and the highwater mark of his career. It was an accomplishment he would never again achieve.

Kafu's position had its hazards. A man who always thought the past better than the present, so much so that the once bad present in due course became the good past, he entrenched himself in an anti-social solitude, which he believed to be ethically necessary. This was to yield the unexpected dividend of popularity in the years immediately following the war (thanks to his uncooperative attitude toward the wartime authorities), but it also resulted in a gradual darkening of tone, a certain cold sardonic note.

During the Rains is considered to be among Kafu's masterpieces by a variety of writers, critics, and scholars, among them Tanizaki Jun'ichiro, Nakamura Mitsuo, and Donald Keene. Edward Seidensticker, in his authoritative *Kafu the Scribbler* (1965), cites a comment by Tanizaki as the most perceptive yet made. I quote from his translation:

The old-fashioned is fairly conspicuous in Kafu's recent *During the Rains*. Indeed in its style and the shifting of its scenes, it might be called the oldest of his novels yet. There are chance meetings scattered all through the book, which are used to further the plot, in a manner common enough in plays and novels of another era. The oldness of the form stands in subtle contrast to the modern colors of the material.

And Donald Keene, in his monumental study of modern Japanese fiction *Dawn to the West* (1984), has this to say:

During the Rains . . . ranks as one of Kafu's finest achievements. . . . The exceptional praise that *During the Rains* won from discriminating critics was occasioned chiefly by the novelistic interest. The detached analysis of a group of people makes the story read like a work of French Naturalism, though a few passages, mainly those relating to Kiyooka's father, evoke the beauty of place and season in the typical Kafu manner.

Flowers in the Shade might almost be called a continuation of *During the Rains*. Of one character, the author says: "In Jukichi's eyes, the lives of respectable people seemed absurdly constricted and somehow hypocritical. By contrast, a lewd, indolent existence such as his seemed the happiness of life without its pretenses" (Chapter 8). And later, of another character, Kafu comments:

This Tsukayama was the owner of an electrical appliance factory, which he had inherited from his father. However, foreseeing the labor agitation that would continually plague the business after the enforcement of universal suffrage, he quickly sold the factory. Distancing himself from the disorders of contemporary society, he passed his self-justified days in reading and collecting antiques. . . . Both by temperament and philosophical outlook, Tsukayama felt an extreme pessimism toward human life. (Chapter 13)

Again, as in so many other cases, Professor Keene's commentary seems the definitive one:

Flowers in the Shade is another example of Kafu's special variety of Naturalism. He makes us see and all but smell the dingy rooms he describes, without ever allowing us to pass judgment on them or their inhabitants. Kafu neither approves or disapproves of his characters, and if he tells us in detail about their past it is not in order to demonstrate how environment and heredity have determined their lives, though this was probably true, but to assuage our curiosity as to how Jukichi came to live off women, how a particular woman happened to become a prostitute or a procuress, and so on. Despite the flaws of narration, *Flowers in the Shade* is unquestionably the work of an exceptional writer. (*Dawn to the West*)

These stories are set in the "second Tokyo" of this century, which succeeded the first Tokyo, destroyed in the Great Earthquake of 1923, and which disappeared in its turn in the American incendiary raids of 1945. Most of the neighborhoods and the neighborhoods within neighborhoods that Kafu so lovingly names and describes have long since vanished, subsumed in the un-neighborhood-like wards.

Kafu's sympathies are clearly with the ladies of the Tokyo demimonde, the geisha-prostitutes, waitress-prostitutes, and out-and-out prostitutes that figure in these stories. A man wedded to the past, happy only in retrospect, an incurable backward-looker, Kafu saw in their world the last tattered vestiges of the licensed quarters of the old city, when it was called Edo. He also saw in their day-to-day life the only honest way to live, the love with the least falsehood, in a materialistic, hypocritical society. One may surmise that among these feckless, irresponsible yet generous-hearted sensualists at the bottom of the social abyss, in the back alleys of Tokyo, Kafu found emotional freedom from the cramped proprieties of his family.

Kafu was not on particularly good terms with his relatives. He fell afoul early on of his rigidly oldfashioned father with his superficial overlay of Western ways; a gradual estrangement developed between himself and his mother over property matters and his unrespectable second marriage to a geisha; and the gulf between himself and his youngest brother was such that Kafu refused either to visit his ailing mother or attend her funeral in 1937 because it would involve seeing the brother. According to Kafu, this brother, among other offenses, had incited his children to behave disrespectfully toward him. Although following the war there was a reconciliation of sorts with the brother, Kafu's relations with his family continued thorny and lacking in affection to the end. Although he adopted a cousin's son during the war, he later tried to return him when he became suspicious of the cousin's motives in agreeing to the adoption.

Ironically, Kafu's sense of nature seemed to require an urban or suburban presence limiting or encroaching upon it, to lend it the poignancy of transience or besiegement. In *During the Rains*, besides the idyllic interlude of Tsuruko's visit to her father-in-law's cottage in the outskirts, soon to be effaced by the expanding metropolis, Kafu left this description of the scenery of the Imperial Palace compound in the heart of Tokyo:

As the path along the top of the embankment gradually sloped lower, at each step the night sky seemed to spread out wider overhead. Visible in a single sweep of the eye from Ichigaya to Ushigome, the scenery along the Moat—the embankment and the trees and shrubberies—was an overall misty green. In the softly flowing night wind, there was the scent of field grass and the grassy-smelling blooms of the pasania trees. From the sky above the towering pine trees across the Moat, there came the sudden call of what sounded like a night heron.

"Ahh—somehow it's as if we were in the country." Kimie looked up at the sky. (Chapter 3)

The stories may be accused of technical faults: the excessive use of coincidence, chance encounters, and happenstance to move things along (although this may have been a quite deliberate return on Kafu's part to the methods of an earlier literature); the inadequate role allotted to Tsuruko, the neglected wife in *During the Rains*; the irrelevant or overly detailed characterization of the heroine Kimie's old landlady; the taking of sides by the author, such as in his sarcastic portrait of the successful pulp-fiction writer Kiyooka and his sympathetic depictions of Tsuruko and Akira, her father-in-law; his attributions of sentiments that seem clearly his own to Jukichi, the paramour of the kept woman O-Chiyo, to Tsukayama, the gentleman of private means and benefactor of O-Chiyo's daughter O-Tami, to Akira (who at one point quotes approvingly from Hosoi Heishu, an eighteenth-century Confucian scholar whose work Kafu was reading on the day of the Great Earthquake, September 1, 1923), and, finally, to Matsuzaki, the genial philandering ex-official who lived down a bribery scandal.

In this they imitate life, where despite our best efforts we are constantly taking sides in our feelings about people, dwelling in detail on those who interest us and perfunctorily dismissing from our thoughts those who don't, and projecting our feelings and thoughts onto others. Perhaps the best reply to critics would be to say that imaginatively Kafu lived these stories and set them down in a manner faithful to his feelings rather than following some abstract set of guidelines for fiction writing. As if to teach us that the most successful works are sometimes those that break all the rules, the stories remain irreplaceable accounts of life in a lost Tokyo, preserved alive in all its touchingly inconsistent human detail, in beautifully perceptive choice of detail, by the medium of a masterly prose style.

After the publication of *A Strange Tale from East of the River*, Kafu fell largely silent during the years of war with China and America. His silence, on the evidence of his wartime diaries, seems to have been based on his contempt for the vulgarity of militarist Japan more than anything else, although it was a silence enforced by the authorities, who judged his work to be frivolous and subversive of the war effort. The few stories from this period, such as "The Decoration" (1942), *Sinking and Swimming* (1942), *The Dancing Girl* (1944), and *A Tale No One Asked For* (1944–45), minor but appealing works set in familiar Kafu milieux, were published after the war. A trickle of stories continued to the end of his life, including some very good ones that reported the hardships of ordinary people in the desperate postwar conditions. An example of these is "The Scavengers" (1948), an account of foraging for food in the countryside around Tokyo.

Kafu's major postwar work was the publication of his diaries for the years 1917–59. Written and styled throughout for eventual publication, they were highly prized by Kafu himself, who kept them always with him; they also rank high in the estimation of some critics. Kafu enjoyed his widest reputation among the general public during the postwar years, mainly as a character whose doings as a penny-pinching eccentric and frequenter of the tackier entertainment districts, especially Asakusa, were reported in the tabloids.

Nakamura Mitsuo, the critic cited earlier in this preface, has left this portrait of Kafu during these years:

I had some slight acquaintance with Nagai Kafu in his later years. Now that I think of it, I have the feeling that he was a man of rather large physique. Not only was he unusually tall for a Japanese of the Meiji era, but the features of his long face were all large also. In particular, he had splendid-looking ears.

In addition, his youthfulness, as symbolized by the nearly jet-black hair that belied his age, remains strongly in my impression of the man.

This large stature and youthfulness of his were not merely the distinctive features of his physique. They also may be said to be important characteristics of his literature.

Nagai Kafu died on April 30, 1959, in Ichikawa, just outside Tokyo. He was buried in the family plot at Zoshi-gaya Cemetery in Bunkyo-ku, the old Koishikawa.

The texts used for these translations are those in *Nagai Kafu Shu*, published by Shinchosha as volume 14 in *Nihon Bungaku Zenshu* in 1961. My grateful thanks are due John R. Ziemer of Stanford University Press for his pains-taking editing and valuable suggestions for the improve-ment of the English versions.

L.D.

During the Rains

ONE

THAT day, Kimie did not have to report for work at the cafe on the Ginza until three o'clock. From her rented room in Honmura-cho in Ichigaya, she strolled out along the Moat [around the Imperial Palace compound]. Boarding a bus at the approach to the palace gates, she got off in Hibiya. This side of the steel railway bridge, she turned off into an alley lined with the banners of eating and drinking shops, like some neighborhood in the suburbs. She was looking for the window of a rented office with a sign in gilt characters that read "The Golden Tortoise, Divination and Fortune-telling."

Since the close of the previous year, Kimie had had several strange, disturbing experiences. Once, on the way back from the kabuki with two or three fellow waitresses, the cuffs of all her sleeves, from her sealskin coat to her matching haori* of Oshima pongee and her padded silk jacket clear through to her undergarment, had been slashed off by a mysterious passer-by. Then, an ornamental comb of genuine tortoiseshell inlaid with pearls had been pulled out of her hair while she was unaware. If it was done by a thief, that was that. What made her feel that it was the handiwork of someone with a grudge against her, however, was the fact that subsequently a dead kitten had been tossed into her clothes closet. Even though Kimie had been leading a really wild, abandoned

*A light, short coat worn over the kimono (tr. note).

3

life these past months and years, think as she might, she had no memory of having done anything to incur such enmity. At first, she had merely thought it odd and not paid it much mind. Recently, however, in a small trade tabloid called *Street Scenes*, which mainly retailed gossip about the women who worked at the cafes and restaurants on and around the Ginza, something about her had appeared that until then Kimie had thought no one could have known. Suddenly uneasy, she had decided to follow her friends' advice and consult a fortune-teller.

The article in *Street Scenes* had been neither slander nor defamation. On the contrary, it was a harmless and inoffensive article, brimful of praise for Kimie's beauty. It told how as a young girl Kimie had had a mole on her inner thigh, said to be a sign that when she grew up she would enter one of the entertainment professions. After she had become a waitress, at some time or other the mole had split up into three moles. No doubt, the article continued, Kimie must be secretly overjoyed and in a state of suspenseful anticipation over this sign that she would find three patrons. When Kimie read this, it had given her a truly unpleasant, ominous feeling. It was certainly the case that on her left inner thigh a mole which had at first been by itself had been joined by two other moles without her exactly noticing when. It was the absolute truth. Kimie had first noticed the moles at about the time she had gone to work on the Ginza, having started out at a cafe on Ueno Pond the previous spring. There were only two men who could have known about them. One was Matsuzaki, a lusty old gentleman with whom she'd been having an affair since her pre-waitress days. The other was a writer called Kiyooka Susumu, who had surged into popularity since she had met him at the cafe in Ueno. The location of the mole was such that not even her family could have been expected to know about it. Even the attendant at her bathhouse could not have been that observant. Kimie didn't particularly care one way or another about the moles, but how had a newspaper reporter known about something that even a bathhouse attendant would fail to observe? Joining these doubts to her suspicions from the previous year, Kimie was suddenly possessed by a vague fear. There was no telling what might happen after this, she thought. Although up to now she had never so much as drawn a lot at a temple, let alone performed devotions to the gods, she abruptly felt she ought to see a fortune-teller.

This latter-day wizard, who had set up shop in a single room in an apartment house, was a man of about forty. Dressed in a Western business suit, with celluloid tortoise-shell glasses, he had a clipped mustache. His demeanor, as he leaned against his desk, at first glance was no different from that of a doctor or lawyer greeting his client. Over the window, which afforded frequent views of passing national railway trains, a framed inscription read: "Divine Aid. The Writings of Heihachiro." On the walls, there were maps of Japan and the world. Alongside the desk, a bookcase with staggered shelves held foreign tomes and Japanese books in traditional bindings.

Taking off her light shawl but keeping it in her hand, Kimie seated herself in the indicated chair. The fortune-teller, closing a half-read volume on the desk, swiveled his chair so that he faced Kimie.

"Does it concern marriage? Or shall I tell you your overall fortune in life?" the fortune-teller inquired, a professional smile on his face. Kimie, lowering her eyes, answered: "It doesn't particularly concern marriage."

"Well then, we'll look into more general matters."
Deliberately informal, evidently at pains to put Kimie
at her ease, like a gynecologist inquiring into a patient's
condition, the fortune-teller continued: "Having one's
fortune told is very interesting, it seems. All sorts of
clients come here. Some people even stop by every morning on their way to the office to get their fortune told for
that day. However, from the days of old there has been
no telling whether a prediction will actually come true or
not. Even if you draw a bad reading, there's nothing to
be alarmed about. How old are you?"

"My sign came up this year."

"In that case, your sign would be the sign of the Rat.
What day were you born?"

"The third of May."

"The third of May, in the sign of the Rat. Let's see . . ."
Taking up the yarrow sticks and muttering something
under his breath, the fortune-teller set out the divining
blocks on the desk. "The divination sign for your age is
richūdan. However, if one read out the commentary from
the book, it would probably be long-winded and not to
the point. Therefore I will simply tell you my thoughts as
they occur to me. Generally speaking, people who belong
to this *richūdan* sign, both men and women, tend to be es-
tranged from their relatives and to have very few friends.
They pass through the world alone. Furthermore, judg-
ing from the month and day of your birth, you belong to
the *yukon-senpu* sign. This sign means that even if there
has been an upheaval in your life, things will gradually
revert to normal. As I consider this sign, it seems to me
that you are in transition. There has been a great change in
your life, but now things are slowly returning to the way
they were. If we compare it to weather, there has been

a storm, and it hasn't yet altogether gone away. But it would probably be correct to say that things are quieting down and well on the way back to their original calm."

Kimie, fingering the shawl in her lap, stared vaguely at the fortune-teller. It was not as if this divination had nothing to do with her. Something about it was right on the mark. Feeling somehow embarrassed, Kimie lowered her eyes again. The diviner's saying that there had been a change in her life no doubt referred to her having ignored her parents' advice and run away to Tokyo, where she had ended up as a waitress.

Kimie had left home to escape from a marriage proposal her parents and all her relatives had urged upon her. Kimie's natal house was in the village of Maruen in Saitama Prefecture, about two hours away by train from Ueno Station. The family business was the manufacture of a kind of sweet that had become a noted local specialty. Among Kimie's friends from grade school was a girl called Kyoko, who'd gone on to become a geisha in Ushigome and within a year had been redeemed by her patron and established as his mistress. The two girls constantly visited each other. When Kimie, not caring to become a country wife, had run away from home, she'd gone straight to Kyoko's house. Even though her people had come and taken her back to the country several times, she'd always run away again. At their wits' end, her parents let her go her own way, giving her permission to become an office worker or a bank clerk.

Although Kimie, through the good offices of Kyoko's patron (a man named Kawashima), had presently found work at an insurance company, this was no more than a temporary sop to her parents. Within half a year, she was out of work and spending her days in idleness at Kyoko's place. Suddenly, it was discovered that Kyoko's patron had embezzled company funds. The case was sent to the prosecutor's office. Kyoko began inviting men whom she had known from her geisha days back to her house. When that failed to make ends meet, she went around to assignation houses and marriage agencies for customers. Kimie, observing her friend's easy circumstances, thought it a good way to make a living. At some point, she'd entered the profession herself. But it would be dreadful to be arrested, Kyoko said; she was going back to being a geisha. Although thinking it might be nice to be a geisha, Kimie knew that when one applied for a license, the police were required by law to make inquiries of the girl's family. She'd had no choice but to become a waitress.

Although Kyoko had to send money to her people in the country, Kimie was under no such necessity. A country girl herself, she felt no great need to deck herself out in the latest clothes and accessories and, unless invited, never went to movies and plays. The desultory perusal of a novel or a book of short stories on the trolley was the extent of her amusements. Other than that, she would say, she didn't even know herself what she liked to do. As long as she had enough to pay the rent and her hairdresser, she had no wish to squeeze money out of men. Often, for no extra charge, she had done exactly what the man wanted, so that no matter how lascivious a life she had led, Kimie thought, it was not likely that she had incurred any great degree of dislike from anyone.

"So there is nothing I have to particularly worry about at present?"

"How is your health? If there is nothing particularly the matter at present, then it does not seem to me that you will have any serious health problems in the near future.

As I previously indicated, there has been a disturbance in your life, but now things are quiet, indeed somewhat stagnant. Perhaps you haven't noticed it yourself, but you may have some feeling of uneasiness, of disquiet. However, as I mentioned earlier, according to your divination sign the temporary change in your life is gradually abating, and so I do not think there will be any untoward events from now on. However, if there is something that troubles you, and you are wondering what to do, let us, in regard to that particular matter, take another reading. By that means, I believe, we will obtain a general idea of what it is." So saying, the fortune-teller took up the yarrow sticks again.

"Actually, there *is* something I'm slightly anxious about," Kimie started to say. But it was impossibly difficult to come right out and tell him about the moles. "I don't remember having done anything in particular, but somehow I feel as if somebody has misunderstood me."

"Yes, yes." Closing his eyes in a significant kind of way, the diviner once more counted out the yarrow sticks and placed the divining blocks. "Indeed. This sign signifies that the shadow accompanies the object. It's possible that you are worrying *too much* about various things. In this way, something that is not comes to seem as if it were. To use the language I employed just now, there is illusion and there is actuality. When a thing exists, it naturally casts a shadow. According to time and circumstances, however, the opposite sometimes happens, and the thing is created by the shadow. Therefore, if you eliminate the shadow, matters will be peacefully settled of their own accord. If you will put yourself in such a frame of mind, I believe that you will have nothing to worry about."

Thinking that what the diviner said was extremely

9

plausible, and that she'd been fretting over trivialities, Kimie immediately felt reassured. Although there were other things she wanted to ask about, she was afraid that if she went into detail not only her present occupation but her having made the rounds of the assignation houses and marriage agencies with Kyoko two or three years ago would come to light. It occurred to her that she might ask about the dead kitten and the vanished comb, but she did not want to be late for work. She would leave things as they were today.

"Excuse me, but what is your fee?" Kimie slipped her hand into her obi for her purse.

"My regular fee is one yen, but please give what you feel is right."

The door opened, and two men in Western clothes entered. Not only did they unceremoniously plunk themselves down in the chairs right alongside Kimie's, but one of them stared round-eyed at her as if he were a detective. Averting her face, Kimie got up. Without saying good-bye to the diviner, she opened the door and stepped into the corridor.

When she emerged from the building, in the clear, serene sunlight of early May, the young foliage shone a vivid green all along the Moat from Hibiya Park. In the groups of people waiting for the trolley, the flutter of fashionable clothing caught the eye. Glancing at her wristwatch, passing under the steel railway bridge, Kimie approached Sukiyabashi Bridge. Past the Asahi Newspaper Building, advertisement balloons were moored to the roofs of several of the tall buildings. Unconsciously pausing, Kimie gazed up at the spectacle. Then, behind her, a voice called out "Kimie-san," and the sound of sandals hurried toward her. Wondering who it could be,

Kimie turned around. It was Matsuko, a girl of twenty-one or -two with whom she had worked last year at the cafe on Ueno Pond. Since that time, Matsuko's clothes and general appearance had greatly improved. Guessing from her own experience, Kimie said: "Matsuko-san. You're on the Ginza too."

"Yes. And no." After this ambivalent answer, Matsuko went on: "Toward the end of last year, I spent some time in the Japan Alps. After that, I played around for a while. But now I want to work again. I'm on my way to a bar called the Lenin in the Fifth Chome. You probably know it, Kimie-san. Atsuko, that girl who was with us at the Salon Lac, is there now. So I thought I'd go take a look."

"Oh, you were in the Alps? I hadn't heard. I've been at the Don Juan ever since then."

"Recently, I heard from one of my customers in the Alps. It might be nice to see him again, but I just don't have the time. How is that sensei* of yours? Still the same?"

Kimie, while thinking that the respectful appellation must refer to the writer Kiyooka Susumu, thought it best to subtly sound out Matsuko. Among her many customers, there were also lawyers and doctors, all of them sensei.

"Yes. He's frightfully busy these days, what with the newspapers and films and all that."

Matsuko, however she interpreted this, seemed to be deeply impressed. "Oh, is that so-o-o . . . ?" Taking a deep breath, she went on: "When you come right down to it, men are a coldhearted lot. I've got plenty of experi-

*A respectful term of address applied to teachers, writers, and artists (tr. note).

ence under my belt. That's why I'm thinking of going into business in a big way from now on."

Kimie, thinking in her heart of hearts that there was no need to give the grandiose term "experience" to what at the outside was five or ten men, was amused. Half-teasingly, in a deliberately downcast manner, she said: "The sensei has a respectable wife, and he also has that famous actress Suzuko. A waitress like myself is nothing but a temporary plaything for him."

When they'd crossed the bridge, as they drew near Owari-cho the pedestrian traffic gradually grew lively. However, Matsuko, oblivious of the passers-by, simple girl that she was, immediately blurted out: "But the reason Suzuko got married was because the sensei was in love with you. Everybody says so. Isn't it true?"

Somewhat disconcerted by Matsuko's earnestness, Kimie quickly replied: "Matsuko-san. We'll meet again soon and have a good long talk. If you like, come and see me. They're hiring now at the Don Juan too. I'll give you an introduction."

"How many people do they have there now?"

"Sixty. Two shifts of thirty each. The cleaning-up, tables and everything, is done by the men, so that alone makes it easier than elsewhere."

"How many turns do you have to take?"

"Let's see, now. Lately, it's been best to take three."

"I can't afford fancy kimonos. And once you take a taxi, you end up doing it every night . . ."

When it came to detailed accounts of life's hardships, even though she felt for the other person, Kimie soon grew intolerably bored. Anyway, if it was a matter of money, even without saying anything you were bound to get something from the man. Separated from Matsuko in the crowd, not once looking back, her eyes dazzled by the Mitsukoshi Building bathed in the full sunlight, Kimie briskly cut across the intersection toward the far side of the street. Then, feeling a little ashamed of herself, she turned and looked back. Matsuko, standing just where she had left her, was bowing slightly as a sign of farewell. Then, as if her mind were relieved by that, she turned away and immediately vanished into the crowd.

TWO

Two or three doors down from the Matsuya Dry Goods
Store, toward Kyobashi Bridge, a pair of nude plaster
women, one on each side of a wide archway in a twenty-
five-foot facade, supported a sign in roman letters that
read DON JUAN. At night, the letters were lit up with
red electric light bulbs. This was the cafe at which Kimie
worked. As far as the eye could reach, almost side by
side, the same sort of cafes lined the alley. If you were
inattentive, you might pass by without observing which
was which. Kimie, although she'd been working here for
about a year, still felt as if she might enter the wrong cafe.
Even now, she used the optician's shop this side of the cafe
and the hardware store beyond to locate the alley in between. Although the alley was just barely wide enough to
let one person through, it was lined with enormous garbage cans. Even in the dead of winter bluebottles buzzed
about, and at high noon ancient rats the size of weasels
went about their business at will. When someone approached, they would splash up water from the puddles
with their long tails. Holding back her sleeves, Kimie advanced stealthily ten steps or so. By and by the faces of the
people passing her became familiar. Once she was inside,
the odor of cheap cooking oil assailed her nostrils like a
wave from the kitchen, where numberless "oven bugs"
scurried all about. The kitchen had evidently been built
on behind the restaurant. Unlike the respectable front
entrance on the Ginza, its walls and roof were a single

thickness of corrugated sheet iron, like the shacks that had sprung up immediately after the Tokyo Earthquake.*
Not taking her shoes off, Kimie went up the steep ladder-stairs from the dirt-floored entryway. At the top, there was a ten-mat room with fourteen or fifteen mirrored dressing-stands lined up along the four walls. It was five or six minutes to three. The second shift was arriving to replace the women who'd been working since eleven. In the crowded room, there was no place to sit down. In front of each mirror, two or three girls were competing for space, sticking their faces out, applying the final layer of makeup, altering the style of their hairdos, standing up and changing their clothes, or sitting cross-legged as they put on fresh white socks.

Taking off her vertically slubbed unlined haori, Kimie wrapped it up with her shawl in a carrying cloth. Tucking it away in the pigeonhole marked with her name in the clothes shelf that stood by the doorway, she patted the tip of her nose with the powder puff from her compact. Going along the corridor through the pantry, she encountered a waitress named Haruyo coming from the second-floor dining room. Since their homeward journeys both lay in the direction of Yotsuya, Kimie, among her sixty co-workers, had grown the most friendly with this girl.

"Haru-san. We missed each other last night. I'll treat you to something after work."

"It was your fault. I waited for you the longest time. Let's go home together tonight, though. That way we'll save money."

As Kimie started along the corridor toward the second

*September 1, 1923 (tr. note).

floor front, the man "boy" in charge of footgear called up repeatedly from the bottom of the stairs.

"Kimie-san. Telephone."

"Ye-e-s." Answering in a loud voice, Kimie muttered to herself: "Who can it be? What a nuisance." Trotting with little steps between the tables and the potted plants, she descended the ladder-stairs.

Downstairs was a single large room, all of it visible at a glance, entered from the Ginza through a big stained-glass door. Although large, its space was cluttered with tables and chairs, set up in booths on both sides of single-leaved screens lining the walls to the right and left. From the ceiling, artificial flowers twined around paper lanterns. Below there were not only potted plants among the tables and chairs, but a dense stand of shrubbery, like a stage bamboo thicket, had been installed. Somehow cramped, at first the room gave only an impression of disorder. Set up across one wide corner was the bar, its shelves lined with bottles of foreign liquors. Underneath a large pendulum clock on the wall was the cashier's counter. Next to it, behind a glass door, was the telephone. Kimie, putting on a smile for each person she passed, trotted toward the booth. "Yes? Who is it?" It turned out that the call was not for Kimie but for another waitress called Kiyoko.

Pushing open the glass door with the tips of her toes, Kimie called out: "Kiyoko. Phonecall." Turning inside the booth, arching her head back, she looked around the room. At this early hour, there were but two groups of customers, each with seven or eight waitresses clustered around them. Even when she peered through the leaves of the shrubbery, Kimie saw no sign of Kiyoko. Somebody said: "She must have been on the early shift." Repeating this answer into the phone, Kimie hung up and stepped out of the booth. A thin, middle-aged man in Western clothes called to her from where he was standing at the counter: "Kimie-san. How did it go? The divination."

"I've just gotten back from there."

"And how did it go? Thoughts of a man, after all?"

"If it were that, I wouldn't have to go to a fortune-teller, would I? It's not that kind of thing anymore, Komatsu-san. I'm very pessimistic."

"What? Kimie-san . . ." His narrow eyes crinkling at the corners, the man she'd addressed as Komatsu smiled at Kimie. Forty or thereabouts, he was employed as an accountant at some dance hall in Kanda. Every day, until he went to work at six in the evening, he made the rounds of the cafes where he was known. His greatest pleasure was to do all sorts of favors for the women, finding them rooms, redeeming their things at the pawnshop, buying theater tickets—there was nothing he would not do for them. Made much of by them, he would be greeted with cries of "Komatsu-san, Komatsu-san." If he never said anything unpleasant, on the other hand he never ate or drank anything. In his youth, it was said, he'd been a geisha's attendant, carrying her samisen for her when she went out on engagements. He was also said to have been an actor's valet. It was he who had told Kimie about the fortune-teller in Hibiya.

"Kimie-san, what did he tell you? Did you get any clues?"

"Well, somehow—he told me all sorts of things, but it isn't clear what the matter is. I didn't try asking him anything in particular, myself . . ."

"That's no good. You're too easygoing, aren't you, Kimie."

"I wasted one yen." Only now that she had been asked,

Kimie realized that the diviner's prognostications had been completely beside the point and her questions extremely half-hearted. She should have questioned the diviner minutely and at length, even if it meant making him slightly uncomfortable.

"Even so, Komatsu-san. He said for the time being there's no danger. That's all I found out. He said this and that, but what it came down to was 'the matter is not clear.' He said a mouthful there. Anyway, that's the first time I've had my fortune told. Unless you have it done regularly, it's no good. Maybe fortune-telling, too, depends on what you ask."

"Even if there's a method of divination, there's no method of asking."

"Yes, but when you go to the doctor for the first time, doesn't he tell you that unless you tell him what the matter is, he can't help you? That's why I think it must be the same with a fortune-teller."

From the direction of the front stairs, a plump, beautifully mature waitress in her thirties called Choko approached with a ten-yen note in her hand. "Cash, please." Pausing at the counter, giving herself a good look in the wall mirror, she adjusted the collar of her under-kimono.

"Kimie-san, Ya-san is upstairs. Please go up. He's being a nuisance."

"I saw him before, but it wasn't my shift, so I came downstairs. Is it true that he used to be Totsuko's patron?"

"Yes. She was taken away from him by Yo-san of the Japan Film Company."

As Choko started in chatting, the cashier handed her the receipt and change. Just then, in the mirror over the bar, two figures were reflected from the doorway by the counter that led back to the kitchen. It was the owner of the cafe, a man called Ikeda, and an employee by the name of Takeshita. Rather than bother with greeting them, Choko and Kimie put on know-nothing faces and headed upstairs. Ikeda, a thin-faced, bucktoothed man of fifty or so, had returned from a Japanese settlement in South America at the time of the Earthquake. With his savings, he had opened up cafes in Tokyo, Osaka, and Kobe. He was said to be making quite a lot of money.

When the two women arrived upstairs, Choko took the change to a party of two sitting in a booth against the wall. Kimie went toward a table overlooking the Ginza. There sat the man they called Ya-san.

"Welcome back. I'd completely given up on you of late."

"You took the words out of my mouth. The way you were making out the other day. I've never been so humiliated in my life."

"Ya-san. Sometimes it can't be helped." Sweet-talking him, Kimie drew her chair up so close to his their knees touched. Just as if they were on intimate terms, she extracted a cigarette from his pack of Shikishimas on the table and stuck it between her lips.

Ya-san gave himself out as the manager of an imported car dealership in Akasaka-Tamariike. For a while, he had not only come day after day in the afternoon, when the waitresses were at leisure, but had often taken four or five of them out for supper after work. Occasionally, to show her off, he brought a geisha with him. A man of about forty, he would remove his two diamond rings to display them to the ladies, and hold forth at length on methods of appraisal and estimation of price. Vulgarly self-assured in everything, he was a man to set one's teeth on edge. Since he spent freely, however, the waitresses would swarm around him and treat him with every courtesy. Kimie had already received theater tickets from him on two or three occasions, and once, on a holiday, he'd taken her to the Matsuya and bought her a kimono jacket and a fancy dress collar. She had come to feel an obligation toward him. If he were to invite her out for supper and afterward proposition her, it would not be so easy to refuse him. For that reason, when she was teased by Ya-san, rather than put him off with some flimsy evasion, she thought it better to be open with him. It made for less trouble. Masking his inward chagrin with a smile, Ya-san replied: "Well, anyway, I was jealous. You did me wrong." Deliberately passing it off as a joke to the three or four other waitresses clustered around the table, he continued: "I was sitting right behind you. I heard everything you said. Although there were people around, you were holding hands."

"You're impossible. If you're going to complain like that, I'm not going to the theater with you. I'll go someplace else."

"She's awful, this one." Raising his arm as if to strike her, Ya-san knocked over a bottle of cider at the edge of the table. Screaming all together, the waitresses jumped up from their seats. Some of them not only drew back their long sleeves, but hoisted up the skirts of their kimonos to avoid being splattered by the cider, which was dripping from the table to the floor. Kimie, as the cause of this commotion, felt constrained to bring a dishrag. Holding the edge of her sleeve between her teeth, she swabbed the tabletop. Just then a new party of two or three customers came upstairs. "Welcome." The ripely beautiful Choko advanced to meet them. Before taking their order, she called out in a metal-cutting voice: "Who's on duty here?" "Kimie-san, most likely." At this answer from someone, Kimie, tossing the rag onto the dirt of a flower-pot and

20

singing out "Ye–e–s," trotted with short steps toward the newly arrived guests.

The customers, two gentlemen of fifty or so who both had mustaches, were evidently on their way back from the Matsuya or Mitsukoshi's. Paper-wrapped purchases in hand, after they had ordered black tea, they did not even look at the waitresses but began having a serious business talk. Taking advantage of that, Kimie went and sat down in the booth against the wall where the off-duty waitresses had congregated. On the table, scattered about among newspapers and magazines, were such tidbits as chunks of sweet bean paste, salty rice crackers, and peanuts still in the bag. Whatever their fingers touched, the waitresses would pick up and toss into their mouths . . . They were already bored with such mundane matters as chitchat about movies and gossip about colleagues. Even if they'd been sleepy, it was evidently out of the question to take a nap. With nothing to do, they were simply waiting for the time to pass. Just then, a waitress sitting in one corner of the booth, who'd been flipping through the pictures of a magazine, exclaimed: "My, what a beauty! It's Kiyooka-sensei's wife."

At this, all the waitresses in the booth stuck their faces out over the table. Even Kimie, her cheeks bulging with chunks of sweet bean paste, leaned forward slightly.

"Which one is she? Show me. I still don't know what she looks like."

"All right. Take a good look at her." The waitress held out the magazine right under Kimie's nose. The photograph was of a respectable-looking married woman, seated on a veranda. The caption read: "The Home Life of a Celebrity. The Writer Kiyooka Susumu's Wife, Tsuruko."

"Kimie-san. That's nothing, that sort of thing. If I were

you, I'd want to tear it in half." The waitress who spoke flicked a peanut at the photograph. Originally the wife of a dentist, she'd been forced by hard times to become a waitress. Her name was Tetsuko.

"You're quite jealous, aren't you?" As if surprised, Kimie stared back at Tetsuko. "It's just as it should be. A wife is a wife. I don't have to worry about her."

"You're so practical, Kimie-san," chimed in Yuriko. At one time a dancer, she had changed professions and come to work at the cafe. Then Ruriko, who'd started out as an assistant in a hair-dressing salon, added: "Anyway, the lucky one is Kiyooka-san. His wife is a beauty, and his number two is a famous waitress on the Ginza."

"What do you mean, famous? Cut that out."

Purposely pretending to be angry, Kimie got up and went over to the table of the automobile entrepreneur Yata, whom she'd left in the lurch a while ago. Although aware that she wasn't in earnest, her fellow waitresses looked after her with some show of concern. Ruriko had known Kimie since the days when, moonlighting as a prostitute, she'd encountered the latter two or three times at a brothel. Even after they'd come across each other at this cafe, there seemed to be a tacit agreement between them to guard the other's secret. Aware that neither was likely to take or cause offense, no matter what was said to or by her, Ruriko had a placid expression. Just then, she heard what sounded like somebody pounding on a table. Thinking it might be one of her customers, she looked in the direction of the noise. At that same instant, the business-suited figure of a customer who'd just come up the stairs was reflected in the mirror on the far wall. Immediately recognizing it, Ruriko alerted the others in a low voice. "Oops, it's Kiyooka-sensei."

During the Rains

"Sensei, we were just talking about you." Haruyo, one of Kimie's boon companions, came running up. "There's a good booth over there." Clinging to his sleeve, she led him to the booth in the corner away from the others' eyes. This was Haruyo's solicitude, to ward off any trouble. The automobile dealer Yata, who had come to press his attentions on Kimie, still hadn't left yet.

"I already feel hot just from walking here. I'll have a dark beer or something." Shoving an armful of new magazines and newspapers beneath the table, Kiyooka Susumu took off his brand-new gray felt hat and hung it on a spray of artificial flowers. Clad in a blue serge double-breasted suit and wearing a bow tie, he was thirty-five or -six. Noticeably sharp-featured around the nose and chin, he looked all the more high-strung thanks to his hollow cheeks and large eyes whose whites showed clear around the irises. He wore his hair combed back from the forehead with deliberate carelessness. To anyone's eye, he was the up-and-coming writer. As a matter of fact, he looked just like one of the movie stars that one sees in publicity photos. Although his father was said to be a scholar of Chinese literature, Kiyooka, in his student days at some regional university around Sendai, had had extremely poor marks. After graduation, he had gone around a lot with writers, but it was not until three or four years ago that he'd done anything to attract the attention of critics. Then, however—where had he got the idea?—employing as a source book Kyokutei Bakin's*
The Adventures of Dreaming Musobei, converting the kite of the original into an airplane and tacking on the title
He Flies Everywhere, he'd lifted the book's entire plot and placed it in a contemporary setting. The result was a work

*Late Edo writer (tr. note).

23

of popular fiction that was serialized in a newspaper. By
some happenstance, it was an immense success. It had
been dramatized by actors of the New School method
and even made into a movie. Since then, with each new
book Kiyooka's literary star had risen higher and brighter.
Nowadays, his work was to be found in nearly all the
newspapers and magazines.

"Is this one of your books too, sensei?" Making bold
to pick up a book lying on the table, Haruyo gazed at the
frontispiece. "They haven't made this into a movie yet, I
suppose."

Kiyooka put on a bored look. "Haru-san. Make a
phonecall for me, will you? There's a person called
Muraoka in the editorial department of the *Maruen News*.
Here's the phone number. Call him to the phone and tell
him to get over here on the double."

"Muraoka-san? The one we know?"

Haruyo went off to make the call. Sadako, who was
on duty, brought a dark beer and a small bowl of peanuts.
While pouring the beer, she said: "There are some things
in your stories that really bring back the memories, sensei. Back then, not that I had any chance, but I went to
Kamata for the first time."

"So you've been to Kamata, have you, Sada-san?"
Glass in hand, Kiyooka glanced up obliquely at Sadako.
"Why did you give up?"

"Why, you say. Because there weren't any prospects."

"I'm not flattering you, Sada-san. With a face like
yours, you're a natural for the movies. Probably it's because you wouldn't listen to the director. Women are
just no good for anything unless they have a man behind
them. Even lady writers, until their work starts to sell a
little, have to have a man backing them."

Kimie, a cigarette between her lips, came over and silently sat down by Kiyooka. Back from the telephone, Haruyo reported the other party's reply. Seating herself, she added: "Sensei, it's treat time for everybody. Kimi-chan, what would you like?"

"This is fine for me." Kimie picked up Kiyooka's half-empty glass of dark beer.

"That's certainly nice and friendly. Well then, Haru-chan—you and I will have some chicken rice." Taking a chit pad from her obi, Sadako jotted down the order as she stood up and left.

The shadows of the evening sun that had shone in through the skylight had faded away. From downstairs, abruptly, a phonograph started playing. This was a sign that it was five-thirty. Those waitresses who'd been resting since three now freshened their makeup and went on duty. Upstairs and downstairs, the lights came on. Even though it was still light outside in the long summer evening, inside the cafe, from early on, there was a nighttime liveliness.

 **THREE**

Since their way home lay in the direction of Yotsuya, Kimie and Haruyo usually left the cafe together after work, taking a cab from the vicinity of Sukiya Bridge. Not only would they have been conspicuous on the Ginza, but drunken customers from the cafes thereabouts were still wandering around at that hour. To avoid them, Kimie and her friend would walk on a little beyond the Ginza, hail a passing one-yen taxi,* and board it only after they'd argued down the driver from his original bargain price to thirty sen. That evening, crossing the Sukiya Bridge and passing under the bridge of the Metropolitan Railway, the two neared the Hibiya intersection without having found a cab that would take them.

"What is this? They're making fools of us. Even that one we thought had stopped drove away." Haruyo sounded angry.

"It doesn't matter. Let's just stroll along. I was feeling a little drunk, so it's just the thing."

"It's already high summer, isn't it? Over there by the Moat, it looks just like a stage set."

At the Hibiya intersection, despite the late hour, people were waiting for the trolley.

"Let's economize tonight and take the trolley."

As they headed for the trolley tracks across the wide

*Taxis that provided a ride anywhere in Tokyo for a fixed price of one yen. A yen was worth about $0.50 in 1930's dollars (tr. note).

intersection, a man in a Western suit suddenly stepped in front of them. Surprised, they looked at him. It was Yata, he of the diamond rings, who had been at the cafe that afternoon.

"You're certainly enjoying yourself tonight. Where did you go for a drink?"

"I'll see you home." Yata raised his hand to hail a taxi.

"A trolley is fine for me. The cafe doesn't like it when we get in a car with a customer." Haruyo's polite attempt at a getaway was parried by Yata, who apparently had been brushed off many times in this manner.

"That's for the Ginza, isn't it? If you've come all this way, they won't mind. I'll take responsibility."

"Why not ride on the trolley with us and save some money, Ya-san?" Kimie began walking briskly toward a trolley that had just now arrived, its red lantern signifying that it was the last of the evening. There was no time for Yata to protest. Willy-nilly, he followed the pair and boarded the trolley, which was bound for Shinjuku.

On the trolley, unexpectedly empty, there were three waitresses from some other cafe, unknown to Kimie and Haruyo, and five or six men. All of them were dozing. Until the trolley had passed Hanzomon and was approaching Yotsuya-mitsuke, Yata was meek and submissive, behaving as though he weren't even with the pair. He did not even venture to speak until Kimie, leaving Haruyo behind, was about to get off the trolley. Hurriedly following her off, he said: "Kimie-san, it's too late for a transfer. I'll hail a cab."

"It's all right. I don't have far to go." Kimie began walking along the Moat, deserted of passers-by, in the direction of Honmura-cho. Spotting them, the driver of a one-yen cab put his hand out the window, signaling a discount with his fingers. Another stuck out his grimy visage and jeered at them. Yata stepped up close to Kimie.

"Kimie-san, do you absolutely have to go back? Can't you make arrangements for one night? Eh, Kimie-san? If you must go back, one hour, even half an hour, will do. We'll have a little talk, and then separate right afterward. Please come with me. I won't ask anything unreasonable, and you'll be home before the night is out."

"It's already too late. We've been wasting time. Now I can't go back. Besides, I'm on the early shift tomorrow."

"The early shift? That's eleven o'clock at your cafe, isn't it? While we're talking like this, time is going by. Is around here no good for you? How about Araki-cho or Ushigome?" Gripping Kimie's hand, Yata would not take a single step farther.

As the path along the top of the embankment gradually sloped lower, at each step the night sky seemed to spread out wider overhead. Visible in a single sweep of the eye from Ichigaya to Ushigome, the scenery along the Moat—the embankment and the trees and shrubberies— was an overall misty green. In the softly flowing night wind, there was the scent of field grass and the grassy-smelling blooms of the pasania trees. From the sky above the towering pine trees across the Moat, there came the sudden call of what sounded like a night heron.

"Ahh—somehow it's as if we were in the country." Kimie looked up at the sky. Promptly, Yata suggested: "Why don't we go someplace quiet? Sacrifice one night. For my sake."

"Ya-san, what if we're seen, and there's trouble? Please be my patron, instead of that other person. I'm thinking I'd like to quit the cafe." Meaning to pull at Yata's heart, Kimie purposely rubbed against him as she quietly started walking. Actually, all she had in mind was how to charm Yata into outdoing himself with a really generous tip at whatever place he took her to.

"That person, you say. Who is he? The man you went to the samisen performance with not long ago?"

"No-o-o . . ." Kimie began, then hastily corrected herself. "Yes, yes, that's the one." The man she'd gone to the musical performance with was neither a patron nor a lover. In short, he had been a pick-up customer, the same as Yata.

"Is that so? Is that man your patron?" Taking Kimie completely at her word, Yata continued: "But if he's helped you up to now, it's not a relationship you can give up very easily. It's no good if he nurses a grudge against you."

Kimie stifled an impulse to burst out laughing. "That's so. That's why I said there'd be trouble if anything got out. Tonight will have to be a deep dark secret."

"Don't worry about that kind of thing. Everything's all right. If anything happens, I'll take care of it." Yata felt exultant. Tonight, at least, everything was falling into his lap. Taking advantage of the deserted edge of the Moat, he abruptly held Kimie close and kissed her on the cheek.

Without knowing just when, they'd passed the Honmura-cho trolley stop. They were nearing the foot of Korikimatsu Slope, where the pines stretched out their overarching branches. In the distance, the lights of the Ichigaya station and the police box in front of Hachiman Shrine were visible.

"That police box over there is a nuisance. If it's just a little late, they ask you all sorts of questions. Let's get a cab."

Yata, thinking this was not an opportunity to be

29

missed, looked about him for a cab. Unfortunately, there was not a single one in sight. The pair stood where they had stopped.

"My place is up that alley right over there. You see the drugstore on the corner? At nightfall, an advertisement for Jintan Pills lights up on the roof. That's how you can tell. I'll just drop off my things and come back. Wait for me."

"Hey, Kimie-san. You're sure everything's all right? It'd be a mistake to give me the slip."

"I wouldn't do anything mean like that. If you're worried, come with me as far as over there. Unless I go back, the old woman downstairs leaves the door off the latch all night."

Five or six houses along from the foot of Koriki-matsu Slope, the two turned into the alley. In the abrupt change from the spacious view along the Moat to these cramped back streets, not only did one feel as if one's nose was stuffed, but the shabby little houses that irregularly lined the streets on both sides, although interspersed with wicket gates, shrubberies, and the hedge of Kenninji Temple, breathed out a broken-down, decayed atmosphere of utter poverty. When they'd come as far as a house with a fish-shop sign mounted on its eaves, Kimie, saying: "Please wait here," turned into an alley from under the fish-shop's eaves. Yata, close behind her, started to follow, then held back. It might hurt Kimie's feelings to have him see where she lived. Craning his neck, he peered into the pitch-dark alley. At the sound of a very creaky wicket gate opening and closing, he felt somewhat reassured. But his irresistible desire to see for himself led him step by step along the alley. Suddenly, to his surprise, he stepped right in the middle of what seemed to be a puddle of rainwater. Retracing his steps, he scraped the muck off his shoes on some gravel and a ditch-board by the light of the fish-shop's eaves lantern. Presently, Kimie came back out.

"Oh dear—what happened to you?"

"Nothing. These alleys are muddy as hell. What a stink. It's probably cat or dog shit."

"That's why I told you to wait outside. My, you reek." Kimie backed off from Yata as he edged closer. "I'm wearing clogs. I can't let any of that stuff get on my socks."

As they walked, Yata kept scraping his soles against the gravel. When they'd emerged alongside the Moat, underneath the eaves of the corner house there were stacks of firewood and sacks of charcoal. By the time Yata had completed the task of cleaning off his shoes, a one-yen cab drew up without their having hailed it.

"Kagura Slope. I'll give you fifty sen." Taking Kimie by the hand, Yata got into the cab. "We'll get out at the foot of the Slope. We'll walk a little ways from there."

"All right."

"Somehow I feel like walking all night tonight." Passing his arm around her, Yata lightly drew Kimie to him. Kimie, although complaisantly leaning up against him, nevertheless asked: "Ya-san, where are we going?"

Yata, while thinking what a terrible pretender Kimie was, knew nothing of her previous history. He had the feeling that even if she appeared to know the ropes, she might not be that kind of girl. The best tack would be to treat her as an extremely permissive waitress and let her take things into her own hands. Putting his lips to her ear, he whispered: "To an assignation house. That's all right with you, isn't it? It's late. I know a good place. Or if you know of some place, let's go there."

31

At this unexpected comeback, even Kimie was at a loss. "No, any place is all right with me."

"We'll get out at the foot of the Slope, then. I know a quiet place behind the Ozawa Cafe."

Simply nodding agreement, Kimie turned her eyes outside the window, thus ending the conversation. Soon after, the cab stopped at the foot of Kagura Slope. All the shops were closed. Even the nighttime stalls, which earlier in the evening had had a lively trade, were gone, leaving behind a roadside litter of paper scraps and garbage. At this late hour, only a few eating and drinking shops were still open here and there on the Slope. Aside from infrequent cars steering their way among scattered, erratically weaving customers in their cups, only geishas, cutting across the avenue, appearing and disappearing between one alley and another, were to be seen. Halting in front of the Bishamon Shrine, Yata stared at the mouth of an alley across the way.

"I think it's back along there, Kimie-san. There are puddles. Mind your sandals."

The stone-paved alley was so narrow that two people could not walk abreast in it. Apparently fearful that if he went on ahead he would be given the slip by Kimie, Yata stuck close by her, heedless of his elbow and shoulder brushing against the wooden walls. Leaning on each other to save space, they made their way along the alley. At its end, there was a little fox-god shrine. This side of a low stone wall, the alley ran into another alley. In one direction, it immediately became steps leading downward. Just then, with a quiet clatter of wooden sandals, a geisha appeared, holding her skirts up to keep them from getting dirty. Yata and Kimie leaned aside to let her pass. The geisha seemed unaware of some chaotic-looking curls in the chignon of her disheveled Shimada coiffure, and even her gait was languid. In Yata's eyes of course, and in Kimie's too, it seemed, she lent an added charm to the quiet back alley scene. A typical late night encounter in the entertainment district, they both seemed to be thinking. As if they'd agreed on it, they followed her with their eyes. The geisha, all unaware, slid open the kitchen door of a house at the corner of the alley where it turned left in front of the fox-god shrine. As soon as she was inside, with a lively voice that belied her exhausted demeanor of a moment ago, she called out: "Auntie. It's already too late."

Kimie, who'd listened intently, said: "Ya-san. I've thought of becoming a geisha myself. I really have, you know."

"You have, Kimie-san?" Sounding genuinely surprised, Yata seemed about to inquire further. In a moment, though, they'd come to the front gate of the assignation house they'd been looking for. There were still sounds of activity inside. Calling out "Oi, oi," Yata pounded on the closed gate. Almost at once, there was the sound of a glass door being slid open, and somebody slipping into a pair of wooden clogs.

"Who is it, please?" A woman's voice called out.

"Me. Yata."

"Well, you've certainly taken your time, haven't you?" The maid, coming out to open the gate, changed to a somewhat more formal manner when she saw Kimie. "Please come in."

From the end of the corridor, leading the way past the cedar door of what seemed to be the privy, sliding open the door of an arched entryway, the maid showed them into the four-and-a-half-mat downstairs sitting room at the back of the house. Evidently guests had been here until a moment ago. There was a smell of sake, and cigarette smoke hung heavily in the air of the room. One or two parched beans were wedged into the decorative groove of a red sandalwood table. Bringing out a couple of sitting cushions from a pile in the corner, the maid said: "I'll straighten it up for you right away. We've only just now had a chance to tidy the place."

"Business is really good, then?"

"Oh no. The usual hopeless mess." The maid went off to fetch the obligatory tea and sweets.

"Can't we air the room out a little?"

"It certainly is stuffy." Crawling on her hands and knees, Kimie reached out and slid back the paper door. Beyond the eaves, in the small garden there was an illuminated stone lantern.

"Oh, how pretty. It's like a stage set."

"It's different from the cafe, isn't it. A touch of old Edo, one might say." Stretching out his legs on the stepping stone, Yata lit up a cigarette.

On the other side of the shrubbery, the second-floor window of the house next door was alight. Although its reed blind was lowered, the figure of a woman in a Shimada coiffure, standing as she took off her kimono, was clearly projected against the window's paper door. Kimie quietly pulled at Yata's sleeve to draw his attention. Just then, though, the voluptuous-looking shadow, growing larger and less distinct like a cloud, vanished. There was only a low murmur of voices. Yata, who seemed to have noticed nothing, his legs still flung out on the stepping stone, shed his jacket and loosened his necktie. But Kimie,

During the Rains

until the maid brought tea and then a couple of yukatas,* gazed vaguely at the flickering shadows across the garden. For no particular reason, she was suddenly reminded of the first time she had been taken to an assignation house. Although it had been in Omori, not Ushigome, her sitting with the man on the veranda and gazing at the shadows projected against the paper door of the second-floor window of the house next door on the other side of the shrubbery across the garden, as they waited for the maid to complete the preparations, had been in no way different from tonight. All that had changed were her feelings. Then, she had been afraid of and fascinated by the novelty of the experience; now, completely habituated, she thought nothing of it.

"Kimi-san, what are you going to have? They say all they have is Chinese noodles."

At Yata's voice, Kimie turned around. Having changed into his yukata, he was standing up tying the waistband.

"I'm not hungry." Kimie began to loosen the string of her unlined haori.

Depositing the kimono box in which she'd put Yata's Western suit in a corner, the maid said: "Every room is taken tonight. It's cramped, but how would this one be?" Taking some bedding from the clothes closet by the ornamental alcove, she began to lay it out. Once again sitting down on the open veranda, Yata and Kimie looked out at the garden. More and more, the memories of that first night floated up behind Kimie's eyes.

"You can take your bath any time you like. The water's always hot." The maid left the room.

*A light kimono worn in hot weather or used as a bathrobe or sleeping garment (tr. note).

35

"Kimi-san. What are you thinking about? Change into your yukata." Peering into Kimie's face from the side as if worried about her, Yata took her hand. Still in her haori, Kimie removed the sash that kept her obi in place and the sash band. Taking out the contents of her pockets and laying them one by one on the mats, she looked at Yata and smiled. Three years earlier, when she'd left home and was staying with her girlfriend Kyoko, the latter's patron had gotten her a job as a clerk at an insurance company. Within two months, she had been seduced by the department head and taken to the assignation house in Omori. Although that was the first time she'd actually slept with a man, not only had she observed Kyoko bring men into the house on the sly, but on occasion had slept in the same room as Kyoko and her patron. Like a young girl apprentice in a geisha house, she was thoroughly conversant with everything of that nature. At times, she was stirred up by a violent curiosity. She'd even consented to the department head's proposition as a means of satisfying it. The latter, however, unlike the typical aging philanderer, had been quite put off by Kimie's uninhibited behavior. He'd left the assignation house shortly after their arrival. As she remembered all this, Kimie unconsciously let a smile show at the corners of her mouth. Knowing nothing of her thoughts, but pleased to see her smiling, Yata took her in his arms and held her close.

"Kimi-san, you've decided to be good to me. I was thinking it was no good and had given up hope."

"It's nothing like that. I'm a woman, after all. But a man always tells other men. That's why I tried to get away." Encircled by Yata's arms, leaning back against his chest, Kimie passed her hand inside her haori and unfastening the end of her obi drew it out. The thin, fine-quality garment, twisting slightly, slipped free of her shoulders. Her naked bosom was revealed in all its allure at the opening of her long undergarment of vari-colored striped silk. Yata, his voice increasingly urgent, said: "I may not look it, but you can trust me. I won't tell anyone."

"The gossip at the cafe is a real nuisance. No matter what I do, it's none of their business." So saying, Kimie unfastened and discarded her under-girdle. Cradled by Yata's arms, lying in his lap, she arched her body upward. "Take everything off. Even the socks." At a moment like this, Kimie felt twice the interest in the man if it was her first time with him. Unless she captivated the man to her heart's content, she felt she hadn't done her job. Wondering just when she'd fallen into this habit, Kimie would catch herself at it even as she was being coaxed and cajoled. Trying to stop herself, she found she could not. More even than when the man was handsome, the trait arrogantly asserted itself with an ugly old man or a man she'd at first thought repulsive. Afterward, ashamed despite herself, Kimie would shudder at the memory of the things she'd done.

Tonight, her sudden succumbing to the importunities of Yata, whom ordinarily she thought of as a conceited lout, was thanks to that old bad habit surfacing unaware.

FOUR

THE next morning, Kimie, getting out of the cab she'd taken with Yata at the base of the embankment of the Military Academy, returned alone to her rented room in the alley. When she sat down at her dressing-stand, however, she suddenly felt drowsy. Without the strength even to redo her makeup, she barely managed to slip off her haori. Still in her kimono, she keeled over onto her side. It was only nine-thirty by her wristwatch. Intending to sleep the thirty minutes until ten, she closed her eyes. No sooner had she done so than the bell attached to the latticework door began ringing, and she heard a man's voice. She opened her eyes. It was the unexpected voice of Kiyooka. Startled, Kimie sat up.

Kiyooka only came here in the evenings, when Kimie was on the late shift the next day. Even then, he generally let her know ahead of time, while she was still at the cafe. He almost never came calling unexpectedly like this, on the morning of a day when she was on the early shift. Did he know about last night? He couldn't have found out so quickly, Kimie told herself. Although thoroughly flustered, she put on an innocent expression and called out in a lively voice:

"My, how early you are! Everything's still a mess in here."

When she reached the bottom of the ladder-stairs, Kiyooka had just taken off his shoes and come inside.

The old woman, who was sweeping out the doorway, evidently knew what to say.

"Kimie-san. Even if you don't like it, please take auntie's medicine once more before you go out. I was really surprised last night."

Taking heart at this, Kimie rejoined: "I'm all right now. It must have been those dishes I mixed."

"What happened? Did you get an upset stomach?" Saying this, Kiyooka mounted the stairs to the second floor. In Kimie's room, he sat down by the window.

The second floor was two contiguous rooms, one of six mats, one of three. But aside from a cheap utility chest faced with paulownia wood, a dressing table and some tea utensils on a tray, there was almost no furniture. Even on top of the utility chest, there were none of the usual little knickknacks. In this virtually empty space, the soiled, shabby old mats and the rat-gray walls stood out all the more sharply. Except for a faded, dirty muslin sitting cushion in front of the mirror-stand, there were only a couple of extremely worn cotton and flax kimonos tossed against the base of the wall. Kimie, as was her custom, turned the cushion over before offering it to her visitor. Kiyooka, placing it on the windowsill, mindful of the crease in his trousers, seated himself again.

Beneath the window, on the flat zinc roof whose asphalt covering had begun to peel, stains from mouthwash and traces of face powder thrown out the window mingled with waste thread, paper scraps, and the dust and rubbish swept out every day. Across from this filthy roof were the backs of two-story houses that fronted on the avenue that ran past the gates of the Military Academy. Among the dirty laundry, old blankets, and diapers hung out to dry, there was an incessant noise of sewing machines and the clunking vibrations of a printing press. Combined in cacophony, from the grounds of the Military Academy, came the shouts of commands as the students performed drills, the blaring of bugles and the sound of marching songs. Not only that, but during the day, according to how the wind blew, fine dust from the cinder track of the riding grounds came drifting in through the window onto the mats like ashes, and even left a gritty deposit inside the closed wardrobe. Ever since he'd first been brought back to this room (about a year ago), Kiyooka had been trying to persuade Kimie to move to a cleaner, more pleasant neighborhood. Kimie, however, although politely agreeing with him, had shown no signs of making preparations to move. The furniture was unchanged from a year ago, and it would seem she hadn't bought so much as a single teacup since then. Although Kimie certainly had enough money, there was neither a supper table nor a clothes rack. The electric lamp's shade was still cracked, the same as a year ago. No matter how much time went by, the place looked as if she had just moved in. Unlike others in her trade, Kimie had no taste for displaying pots of flowering plants on the windowsill, setting up dolls or toys on top of the chest of drawers, or pasting picture postcards on the wall. From early on, Kiyooka had realized that she was a strange, eccentric girl.

"It's not necessary to give me any tea. You're probably about to leave for work, aren't you?" So saying, Kiyooka slid himself down, cushion and all, from the window-sill until he was sitting tailor-style on the mat. "I've got some business that will take me as far as Shinjuku Station. That's why I dropped by for a moment."

"Oh. Still, you will have a little tea, won't you? . . .

40

Auntie, if the water's ready, please bring us some." Calling out, Kimie went downstairs. She soon came back up with an enameled brass teapot.

"I hear you went to see a fortune-teller. That article about the mole that appeared in *Street Scenes*—did he tell you who was behind it?"

"No. He didn't tell me anything." Pouring some tea from the little pot into a cup, Kimie went on: "At first, I thought I'd ask him about various matters. But somehow I felt awkward, so I held back. When you think about it, though, it's really strange. It's not likely anyone would have known such a thing."

"If you can't find out from the fortune-teller, you should go to a medium or a fox-diviner."

"A medium? What's that?"

"You don't know? Don't geishas often consult mediums?"

"Yesterday was the first time I ever went to see a fortune-teller. Somehow it seems foolish. That kind of thing doesn't work for me."

"That's why you shouldn't worry. Isn't that what I've been saying?"

"But it's just so peculiar. Because something that was so unlikely to be known was known by someone. It's positively weird."

"Even if you think nobody knows about it but you, there are surprising things in the world. Secrets have a way of leaking out." Kiyooka cut himself short, realizing that he'd said too much. Hastily putting a cigarette in his mouth, he covertly observed Kimie's expression. Kimie, about to say something, remained silent. Holding the half-empty teacup alongside her mouth, she stared round-eyed at Kiyooka. Their eyes met and locked. Kiyooka, pretending to be choking on the cigarette smoke, turned his face aside.

"The best thing is not to worry about it."

"That's true." To make it sound as if she were speaking from the heart, Kimie threw a note of conviction into her voice. Unable to say anything else, though, she slowly drained her cup and quietly set it down. Even if Kiyooka didn't know that she'd spent last night in Kagurazaka with Yata, theirs was a relationship of a good two years. Kiyooka knew just about everything there was to know about her. But she couldn't tell exactly how much he knew of this matter. At times, Kimie even felt that at some opportune moment she would like to break off with Kiyooka and make a fresh start with a new lover who knew nothing of her past. Kimie did not like having half her life known about by other people. Even if there was no need to keep something secret, when she was asked by others about it she would simply put them off with a smile, or tell the first lie that came to her lips. Even with her own family, with whom she might have been expected to be the most intimate, Kimie had in fact been the most distant, never divulging her innermost feelings. With a man whom she liked, she was even more secretive. When the man attempted to question her deeply, she sealed her lips more and more firmly and told him nothing. Among her fellow waitresses at the cafe, it was said that no one had a more graceful, genteel appearance than Kimie but that it was impossible to tell what she was thinking most of the time.

Kiyooka had known Kimie ever since the night of her first day as a waitress at the cafe called the Salon Lac on the pond in Shitaya. Kiyooka's first impression of Kimie was that if she hadn't been working as a waitress she most

42

likely would have been a geisha. Her features were rather
average; nothing about them stood out. Her forehead was
round, her eyebrows thin, her eyes narrow. In profile,
her face was extremely concave, as if it had been scooped
out. But the hairline of her "Mount Fuji" brow was as
sharply defined as if she were wearing a wig, and there
was an indescribable charm about her mouth, with its
protruding lower lip. As she spoke, the tip of her tongue
as it moved about between the regular rows of her teeth
like pearls was particularly winsome. Apart from these,
the whiteness of her skin and the gently sloping shoulders
of her figure seen from behind were probably foremost
among her points of beauty. That first evening, Kiyooka
had been especially taken with her quiet manner of speech
and the absence of any vulgarity in her demeanor. Tip-
ping her a munificent ten yen, he lay in wait for her outside the cafe. Unaware that he was following her, Kimie
walked as far as the intersection, where she boarded the
trolley for Waseda, changing at Edogawa. By the time
she reached Iidabashi, where she had to change again, the
last trolley of the night had already left. Kiyooka, who'd
been trailing her in a taxi, at this point stealthily alighted
from it. Pretending that this was a chance encounter, he
engaged Kimie in conversation. Even when asked, however, Kimie would not tell him exactly where she lived.
Merely answering that it was in Ichigaya, she strolled
with Kiyooka along the Outer Moat to the foot of the
Osaka Slope. She gave all the signs of a woman who was
prepared to do whatever the man said.

Shortly before this, with many tears of farewell, Kimie
had parted from Kyoko, with whom she'd been living for
so long and plying the same trade of unlicensed prostitution. Kyoko, finally giving up the house in Suwamachi

of Koishigawa, had moved to a geisha house in Fujimi. Kimie was living by herself on the second floor of a house in Honmura-cho. Since she no longer frequented the prostitution agency, she hadn't slept with a man for more than a month now. It was rare for her even to be out this late at night nowadays. Just the sight, after so long, of the quiet late night scenery along the Moat gladdened her heart in some indefinable way. It was early in May just then, and there was the pleasant sensation of the night wind caressing her skin at the openings of the sleeves and under the skirts of her lined kimono. Thinking that Kiyooka was a young university professor or the like, Kimie had from the start been well disposed toward him. Deliberately repressing her leaping happiness and assuming a constrained air even while going along with him, she let him take her that night to an assignation house in Yotsuya-Arakicho. Innately fickle, Kimie, when she'd found a man, would instantly be passionate for him and as instantly lose interest in him. Her lovemaking with Kiyooka continued almost into the evening of the next day. In her reluctance to let him go, she took that day off from the cafe. Going with him that night to an inn in Inogashira Park, she spent the third night in Maruko Gardens. The fourth day, she returned with him to her rooms in Ichigaya, where they finally parted from each other.

At about this time, Kiyooka had been thrown over by a movie actress called Suzuko something or other, who for a while had served as his concubine. Since her theft by another man, he'd been searching for a replacement. Completely overwhelmed by Kimie's ardent attitude, as if she'd given herself up body and soul to his pleasure, he told her he would indulge her in any luxury she wished and that she was to give up being a waitress. But Kimie said that she meant to open up a cafe herself in the future and would like a little more experience. In that case, said Kiyooka, she should work on the Ginza. Making her quit her job at the Salon Lac after a month or so, he took her around Kyoto and Osaka for a couple of weeks. Upon their return, he got her a job at the Don Juan, one of the prominent cafes on the Ginza. Soon thereafter, the rainy season came to an end and it was summer. From midsummer to the days when the first autumn breezes began to blow, Kiyooka had no doubt but what he was loved by Kimie from her heart. One evening, however, on his way back from the theater with two or three fellow writers, he stopped in at the cafe. Told by the other waitresses that Kimie, complaining of suddenly feeling unwell, had gone home early, he decided after parting from his friends to go by himself to her rented room in Honmura-cho and see how she was. As he set out, he saw a woman's figure suddenly emerge from the street along the Moat that he always turned into. Although it was not yet midnight, the houses along the one side of the alleyway had already shut their doors. Along the thoroughfare, where both pedestrians and trolleys had become sparse, only a solitary taxi raced by. From a distance of about thirty feet, Kiyooka soon ascertained that the woman was wearing a whitish gauze silk-crepe kimono and a summer obi with a pattern of green bamboo. His suspicions aroused, he cut across the roadway. Keeping to the sidewalk along the foot of the embankment, he shadowed the woman. The woman, briskly and blithely passing in front of the police box, seemed to stop and be waiting for a trolley at the Ichigaya stand. Then, unexpectedly, she entered the gate of the Hachiman Shrine. Without looking behind her, she made her way up the Woman's Slope on the left.

Although more suspicious than ever, Kiyooka was determined to stay out of sight. Well acquainted with this neighborhood and trusting to his man's fleetness of foot, he ran around the shrine compound and climbed the Sanai Slope. Entering the shrine grounds from the back gate, he looked about. A man and woman were sitting close together on a bench at the bottom of the stone stairs of the main shrine, where a cliff overlooked the Moat and the Ichigaya Approach. Of course, theirs was only one of three or four benches, on each of which a couple was sitting rubbing shoulders in an illicit rendezvous. Kiyooka, thinking this an excellent opportunity and with a grove of cherry trees as his cover, gradually crept nearer. He wanted to eavesdrop on Kimie and also find out what sort of person her companion was.

Telling himself that no detective in any detective story had ever succeeded in his investigations as he had that night, Kiyooka, at that moment, in the excess of his surprise, had no time to spare for an outburst of jealous anger. The man, wearing what looked like a panama, had on a dark blue yukata without even a summer haori over it and held a walking stick. Although he did not appear to be particularly old, even by the dim light of the park lamp the whiteness of his mustache stood out to the eye. Clasping Kimie around the waist under her obi, the man said: "It certainly is nice and cool up here. Thanks to you, I'm having some new experiences. I never thought that at sixty years of age I'd be meeting a woman on a park bench. Even now, I believe, there's a big archery range on the other side of this shrine. When I was young, I used to come and practice my archery there. Since then, it's been decades since I climbed these stone stairs. Well now, where shall we go from here? Just staying here with you

46

on this bench is fine with me. Ha–ha." Laughing, the man kissed Kimie on the cheek.

For a while, Kimie silently allowed the old gentleman to do as he pleased. Presently, though, she quietly got up from the bench. Bringing the front skirts of her kimono together, and smoothing her sidelocks, she said: "Let's walk a little." Accompanied by the man, she went down the stone stairs. Kiyooka, circling around to the Woman's Slope up which Kimie had come, followed them at a distance. Unaware of him, the pair strolled along chatting by the edge of the Moat.

"How has Kyoko been doing since she moved to Fujimi-cho? A girl like her must surely be very busy."

"She says she's booked up every day from afternoon on. I paid her a little visit recently. But there was no time to have a really good talk. You should go over sometime. It doesn't particularly matter if she's not in."

"Hm. It'd be interesting for the three of us to stay up through the night together. It's been a long time since we had such fun on that second floor in Suwamachi, hasn't it? You and Kyoko were really good playmates. During the day, even when I'm doing some serious work, something odd occurs to me and right away I think of you. Then I think of Kyoko. I feel as if I'm having a dream."

"Still, compared to Kyoko, I'm better for your health."

"I'm not so sure. Just because you look like a decent girl, yours is the greater sin. Aren't things different since you started working at the cafe? What about that foreigner?"

"There's too much gossip on the Ginza. One can't do as one wishes. On the other hand, geishas operate in the open and have no problems. It really was better when I was in Suwamachi."

47

"What about her patron? Has he gotten out of jail yet?"

"I don't believe so. There haven't been any talks since then, so their relationship is probably over. Anyway, it was just obligation—she owed him for having paid off a debt. She wasn't particularly fond of him or anything."

"What does she call herself these days? Is it still Kyoko?"

"No. She calls herself Kyoyo."

Enjoying the cool late night breezes and the pleasantly deserted bank of the Moat, the two flirted with each other as they strolled along. Rounding the New Approach, from the trolley avenue at the base of Hitoguchi Slope, they turned into an alley in Sanban-cho, stopping outside a geisha house that had the name "Paulownia Blossom House" written on the lanterns hanging from its eaves. Since it was a summer night, all the geisha houses in the neighborhood were still open. Geishas sat outside on benches enjoying the evening cool and gossiping among themselves. In a familiar tone, the man inquired: "Is Kyoyo in?" Immediately, a diminutive woman stuck her round face out the door. Clad only in a loincloth, her hair done in a low Shimada coiffure tied with paper cords, the woman emerged from the house in all her nakedness, coming as far out as the dirt-floored entryway.

"Ah, you're together. I'm delighted to see you. You've come at the right time. I've only just gotten back."

"Do you know some good place where we can go and have a nice talk?"

"I see . . . well, in that case . . ." The naked woman whispered an address to the man. The two walked on and turned the corner.

Kiyooka, who up to now had been trailing the pair while keeping himself concealed in the shadows of the alley, could not bring himself to turn back now that things

48

were progressing so satisfactorily. Timing his visit, he proceeded to the assignation house where Kimie had been taken. Posing as an ordinary customer, he paid in advance, asking for a submissive young geisha and took her off to bed quite as if that were all he had in mind. . . . After a night spent with his eye glued to the peephole watching the frolics of that unknown old man with Kimie and Kyoyo, he quietly took his leave before the sun was up. Since it was still somewhat early to return to his house in Akasaka, he had no choice but to loiter a while in the embankment park in Yonban-cho. Strolling or sitting down on a bench, he vaguely gazed at the high ground on the far side of the Moat.

Never, in all his thirty-six years, had Kiyooka seen even in dreams what he had witnessed with his own eyes the night before. He realized that the view of women which he had held up to now was completely mistaken. Without the energy for an explosion of jealous rage, he merely felt unaccountably depressed. Until now, he'd simply assumed that all young women, not just Kimie, calmly surrendered themselves to old lechers in their fifties and sixties, forgoing love and sexual satisfaction solely for the sake of economic security. How wrong he had been! The truth was something quite other. Somebody like Kimie, who he had thought loved him and him alone, had to go and debauch herself with an ugly old man and a lewd, cheap geisha. Along with the realization of how superficial his experience and observation had been, Kiyooka felt a hatred for Kimie that was beyond words. He would never see her again after this. However, after he'd gone home and gotten a little sleep, his roiled-up feelings calmed down considerably. It would be too contemptible for words if he pretended to know

49

nothing. He could not rest easy until he'd confronted her with what she had done and exacted a confession and an apology from her own lips. After further thought, however, he realized that Kimie was not the ordinary girl she appeared to be. Interrogated, she might confess to everything with surprising nonchalance. She might even, in her heart of hearts, be smiling scornfully at his jealousy and sexual frustration. This, for a man, would be a humiliation more difficult to endure than the woman's unfaithfulness. He could not ignore the insult. And it would be even more mortifying to have her ostensibly apologize and then stick out her tongue at him behind his back. After much thought, he decided that he would after all pretend not to know. On the surface, things would be as before. While endlessly being made a fool of, he would bide his time and exact some signal revenge. This was the best plan.

For the past several years, to manage his literary affairs, Kiyooka had made use of two trusted assistants. One was a young writer named Muraoka, who'd recently graduated from Waseda University or some such institution. For a monthly compensation of about one hundred yen, he took down the stories that Kiyooka dictated to him and worked them up into a presentable manuscript. Then Komada, a man of about fifty, went around selling the stories to newspapers and magazines. As a former employee of the accounts department of a newspaper, Komada was conversant with the current prices for manuscripts and also had many friends among the reporters. He worked for a commission of 20 percent. It was the devoted Muraoka who, on Kiyooka's orders, had waylaid Kimie on her way back from the kabuki and slashed off her sleeves with a safety razor. Of course, the garments had been bought for Kimie by Kiyooka. Some time afterward, when they were riding together in a taxi, Kiyooka had stealthily abstracted from Kimie's hair the pearl-inlaid comb he'd bought her at Mitsukoshi's as they were getting out. Contrary to his expectation that she would cry and carry on, Kimie didn't seem to particularly mind the loss. She didn't mention it to Kiyooka or, apparently, to the old woman at her place.

Although Kiyooka had known for some time that Kimie was a slovenly, uneconomical person who didn't look after her affairs properly, he had not imagined that her indifference even to the clothes she wore ran to this degree of nonchalance. Whereupon, when she was out, he'd tossed a dead kitten into her clothes closet and later carefully observed her reaction. Even this, however, had not seemed to sow the seeds of fear in Kimie to any great extent. Finally, although worried that if worse came to worst he would be found out, he had instructed Muraoka to plant an item in *Street Scenes* about the mole on Kimie's inner thigh. This did seem to have caused Kimie considerable uneasiness. Saying to himself "look at that," Kiyooka found a measure of relief from his angry feelings. Now that the scales had dropped from his eyes, however, the more he investigated Kimie's life the more he found to be angry about. His desire for revenge was not to be satisfied by simple occasional pranks. In order to spy out an opportunity to inflict harsher punishment on Kimie's body and mind, he pretended to be more deeply infatuated with her than ever. This was to put her off her guard and to prevent his intentions from being discovered. But the enmity that lay coiled at the bottom of Kiyooka's heart had a way of inadvertently showing itself at the edges of his words. Kiyooka had to exert extraordinary efforts to keep it hidden.

A moment ago, when Kiyooka had despite himself said

too much about the fortune-teller, his frantic attempt to pass it off as nothing was inspired by this concern. It was not good to go on facing each other like this, he thought. Glancing at his wristwatch, he said as if quite surprised: "It's already ten-thirty. I'll go with you."

Kimie, for her part, found it somehow unbearable to be seen by a man in her unwashed state after having spent the night out. She, too, wanted to get out of the house.

"Yes. Let's walk a little. When the weather's so beautiful, I hate to go to work. Because I don't see the sun from one end of the day to the other." Throwing over her shoulders a vertically striped unlined haori that she had carelessly tossed aside, Kimie slid shut the paper window.

"If you go today at eleven, that means you go tomorrow at five."

"Yes. So come to the cafe tonight. I'd like to go somewhere and enjoy myself. Is that all right with you?"

"That's so." Giving this ambiguous reply, Kiyooka took up his hat.

"We'll go somewhere and have a good time, won't we? Anyway, I'm free tonight." Pressing herself against Kiyooka, who already stood at the head of the ladder-stairs, putting up her cheek as if to say "kiss me," Kimie half-lowered her long eyelashes.

Although thinking she was a sly puss, as he looked at this charming, sensuous woman for whom he had no fundamental dislike, Kiyooka reflected that perhaps it was overly severe to find moral fault with a woman born to the trade of pleasure. At that moment, even his long-cherished anger with her evaporated. If one thought of her as a kind of machine for exciting men's sexual desires, what she did when he wasn't around was nothing to punish her for. He even felt as if he should simply extract all the pleasure from her he could and then throw her

52

away. But then, instantly, his wish for her to be a little more considerate of his feelings, to behave herself, and to belong to him and him alone began to surface again. Looking aside, Kiyooka remarked casually: "At any rate, we'll meet on the Ginza tonight. We'll decide then."

"Yes. Please." Her face suddenly brightening, Kimie clattered down the stairs a step ahead of him. Snatching a cleaning rag from the old woman, she wiped off Kiyooka's shoes with her own hands.

In order to avoid the public gaze on the sidestreet that led out to the Ichigaya side of the Moat, the two slipped from alley to alley, coming out in front of the Military Academy. Ascending Bikuni Slope, they walked along the Moat through Honmura-cho in the direction of the Yotsuya Approach. As it was getting toward noon, they kept somewhat apart, although walking side by side, and did not even speak to each other. Kimie, her face hidden by a parasol, abruptly recalled that it was along here that she had strolled hand in hand with Yata the night before, when they'd gotten off the trolley. The contrast of night and day made her wonder, despite herself, what had inclined her to do the will of a man as unsatisfactory as Yata. She could not but feel disgust at her feckless acquiescence. If Kiyooka-san found out about it, how angry he would be. From the shade of her parasol, she furtively observed the man's profile. She felt a slight pang of conscience, and an unbearable sense of pity for him. From now on, Kimie thought, she would behave herself as much as possible on her way home from the cafe and not give in to any impromptu solicitations. It wasn't that she meant it as an apology, but somehow Kiyooka suddenly became dear to her. Snuggling up to him, she took his hand regardless of the passers-by.

Kiyooka, evidently thinking that Kimie had grabbed

his hand because she'd stumbled on something, fearful of the eyes of the public, dodged away from her slightly toward the Moat. "What's the matter?"

"I want so much to take today off. I'll call them up and say I can't come. It'll be all right."

"What will you do the rest of the day?"

"I'll wait for you somewhere until you've finished your business."

"We'll be able to see each other tonight. You don't have to take the day off, do you?"

"I suddenly feel like doing nothing all day. Don't let me stand in the way of your business, though."

Kiyooka had in fact no business to attend to. He had come out on a surprise spying mission to observe Kimie's behavior. If he shook her off at this point and went on his way, he could not be certain of what she might get up to in the interval until he met her that night. The trivial matter began to get strangely on his nerves.

Kimie, for her part, knew from her months and years of experience in manipulating men that in a situation of this kind it was best to give the man a bit of a hard time with her selfish whims. Somehow, Kimie felt intolerably bothered by what Kiyooka had said before about the fortune-teller. Without waiting for tonight, she would have to adopt some method forthwith of making the man say what was in his heart. From long experience, she knew that no matter how angry the man was, when it came right down to it she could easily captivate him. Kimie felt endlessly at ease in this belief in her own glamor. It was something she had been born with, a kind of flesh temperature and body scent that, without her particularly exercising any skill, left the man who had come into contact with it an indelible, lifelong memory of pleasure. Not by one man, not by two men, but by many various men Kimie had been told that she truly was an enchantress. Did her body give men such a powerful thrill? she'd wondered. As she'd become more self-aware, Kimie had gradually perfected her charms until now, despite herself, she believed profoundly in her power of seduction.

They'd come almost as far as the exit of Yotsuya Station. Abruptly putting on a sad, forlorn expression, Kimie said: "I've spoken selfishly, and that's bad. I'll take a one-yen taxi from here."

"Hm." Despite his curt reply, Kiyooka, noticing Kimie's wistful demeanor, felt a curious reluctance to part from her, as if she were a mistress he'd acquired just today or yesterday. Kimie, deliberately fastening a vague gaze on Kiyooka, poking the gravel with the tip of her parasol, stood as if rooted to the ground.

Forgetting everything he had against her, pressing her to him, Kiyooka said: "It's all right. Take the day off. Any place is fine. We'll go together."

"Do you really mean it?" Expertly bringing the tears into her long-lashed eyes, Kimie quietly looked at the ground.

FIVE

In front of the gate of Matsukage Shrine in the metropolitan suburban district of Setagaya, there is a T-shaped
intersection. As you go along the branch road two hundred and fifty yards or so, you come to a red lacquer
gate with a framed tablet that reads "Katsuenji Temple."
Across from it, there is a tea field. From here, the road
goes downhill. There is a view, far in the distance across
dry fields and paddies, of the bamboo grove and cedar for-
est at the back of Gotokuji Temple. Even in Setagaya, this
neighborhood is probably the most secluded and remi-
niscent of the outskirts of the city in the old days. On
the other side of the tea field, there is a row of Western-
style houses with cement gateposts and fences. At the
foot of the slope, however, there are four or five reed-
thatched farmhouses, each enclosed by the same kind of
hedge fence. Among them was an enclosure which, from
the nature of the locality, one might have guessed was the
residence and place of business of a gardener. Double sliding doors were set between "inverted mixing-bowl" gateposts of chestnut wood. Not even the roof of the house,
standing far back among the trees, could be seen from the
street through the luxuriant mass of freshly green foliage.
On one gatepost, a nameplate read "Kiyooka Residence."
The words were rain-stained and difficult to make out.
This was the retirement retreat of the writer Kiyooka
Susumu's old father, Akira. Directly overhead, the early
summer sun shone down on the chestnut and chinaberry

trees just inside the gate. The young leaves' shadows, cast on the ground outside the gate, were drawn up directly underneath the leaves. Only the lusty cluckings of chickens were heard here and there. It was midday.

Closing a sober, burnt-tea-color parasol, a young woman of about thirty, refined-looking and evidently a married lady, opened the gate and passed inside. Her hair done in a loose bun, so that it tumbled casually down onto her nape, she wore a black summer haori with her family crest at the back of the collar over a fine-quality lined kimono with a splash pattern. Her slender, willowy figure, a white shawl over her shoulders, combined with her long neck, well-defined features, and pale, narrow face to give her a tranquilly lonely air. Shifting to the other hand a bundle wrapped in a carrying cloth, she closed the gate. In contrast to the sun pounding down on the road, here a gentle current of air came flowing from the quiet summer shadows of the trees. Stroking back into place a stray curl disheveled by the breeze, for a while the young woman looked about her. The little path inside the gate was bordered with dragon's beard. To one side, chestnut, persimmon, plum, jujube, and similar trees flourished densely. To the other side, there was a grove of speckled bamboo. Its young, vigorously lengthening sprouts were starting to grow up into pale young bamboo trees. From among the branches of the older trees, slender leaves were constantly fluttering to the ground. The heavy-scented flowers of the chestnuts were in full bloom. The young leaves of the persimmon, excelling even those of the Japanese maple, were displaying just at this time their tenderest hues of fresh new green. Filtered by the treetops, the sunlight shifted sparklingly over the thick moss. Beneath the quiet whispering of the breeze, there was a sound of water flowing nearby. Some unknown little bird was warbling, livelier than the shrike singing at the dawn of a clear autumn day.

Unconsciously softening her tread at the sound of the bird's voice, the young woman followed the curve of the gravel path around the bamboo grove until she came to an old bungalow hitherto obscured by the foliage. The entryway had a frosted glass latticework door, but this had evidently been put in as an afterthought. The bungalow itself had a look of timeless stability that brought to mind the priests' living quarters of an old temple. But there were signs that its foundation posts and sturdy housebeams had been spliced to replace rotten wood, and its roof tiles were stained green with moss. Although a tall window alongside the entryway had been left open, not the least sound came from inside the house. Beneath the window, a mixed hedge of box and azalea blocked any view of the garden. But in the sunlight that shone through here, the peony flowers, a mingling of white and red in full bloom, were all the more conspicuous. Here also, however, it was quiet and deserted. There was the sound neither of flower shears nor of a garden broom. Only, on the grape trellis that hung along the eaves to the kitchen door, among the flowers whose time to bloom had evidently come, the buzzing of horseflies gathered in clusters there noised abroad the news that the summer day was long.

"Is anyone home?" Taking off her shawl, the young woman quietly slid open the lattice door. From within the hushed interior, a voice answered: "Who is it?" The opaque paper door was immediately slid back by an old man with his spectacles pushed up on his forehead above his snow-white eyebrows. It was the householder, Akira.

58

"Tsuruko, is it? Please come in. Today the old woman is off on a grave-visit. And I've sent Densuke into the city on an errand. I'm all alone."

"I came at just the right time, then. Perhaps there's something I can do for you instead." Still carrying her bundle, the young woman followed the old man inside and seated herself at the threshold of the veranda.

"You're already airing things out, I see."

"I don't do it at any particular time. I have no help, so whenever the spirit moves me, I do it at odd times throughout the year. It's the best sort of exercise for an old man."

From halfway along the veranda to the eight-mat room at the back of the house, folding cases of manuscripts, scrolls, and pictures had been set out. Both the translucent and the opaque paper doors were wide open. A swallow-tail butterfly came fluttering into the parlor. Presently, it flew out into the garden again. Undoing her kerchief bundle on her lap, Tsuruko said: "I've had that article of clothing made over for you. I'll leave it over there. And while I'm at it, shall I make some tea?"

"Yes. I'd like a cup. I think there's some sweet bean paste or some such thing I got as a gift in the breakfast room. Just have a look, will you?" As Tsuruko got to her feet, the old man began to straighten, one by one, the old manuscripts lying on the veranda. His closely cropped hair, with his thick eyebrows and mustache, had turned as white as snow, accentuating the healthy flush of his face. His lean, slightly built body seemed to have grown more and more vigorous with age. When Tsuruko came back with green tea and sweets, the old man sat down at the edge of the veranda.

"I haven't seen you for some time. I thought you might

have caught a cold. They say the flu is still making the rounds in the city."

"You haven't caught a single cold since last year, have you, Father?"

"I had a somewhat different upbringing from today's young people. Ha-ha. The drawback is that healthy people go off all at once. You can't depend on good health."

"Well—there's no need to say that kind of thing."

"There's a saying from the old days about things you can't trust. 'It is a hard thing to trust in the favor of a lord; it is a hard thing to trust in the health of old age.' Ha-ha. How's Susumu? Flourishing like the green bay tree?"

"Yes. Thank you for asking."

"There's something I've been wanting to talk with him about. Actually, not long ago, I met your elder brother on the trolley . . ." the old man began, then coughed and looked at Tsuruko over his spectacles. Tsuruko, for her part, answered with studied casualness.

"Is it something about me?"

"Yes. It was nothing bad. We were talking about what to do with your family register. There's no use fretting about what has already happened. Let bygones be bygones. I said I had no objections to whatever was decided. If your family and I agree on it, Susumu isn't likely to say anything. What about it, then? If we set about it early on, we can ask the clerk at the ward office to write it up. It's just a matter of my putting my seal to it."

"Yes. I'll tell my husband that as soon as I get back."

"It doesn't really matter about the family register, but it's best to be upright in all one's dealings. If you've lived together the same as man and wife for all these years, it should be a matter of course to enter your name in our family register. I don't really know what went on at first, but according to your brother it's already been five years."

"Yes. If I remember correctly." Deliberately ambiguous, Tsuruko lowered her eyes. She knew, without needing to count the years on her fingers, that it had been five years. In the autumn of her twenty-third year, when her former husband had graduated from military college and was studying abroad, Tsuruko had fallen into a liaison with Kiyooka Susumu at a hotel in Karuizawa. Her husband's family, although not particularly wealthy, were descended from the old aristocracy and as such were fearful what people would hear and say. Without waiting for the husband's return, they'd dissolved the marriage on the pretext of Tsuruko's frail health. Her parents had already died by this time. Tsuruko's elder brother had made something of a name for himself in the world of industry. Bestowing just enough capital on Tsuruko so that she would not go hungry or lack clothing, he forbade her to set foot in the family's house or those of relatives for the rest of her life. At that time, Susumu was still living at home with his father in Komagome-Sendagimachi and putting out a coterie magazine in conjunction with a few other literary-minded youths. When Tsuruko's marriage was annulled, he immediately left his father's house and set up a new household in Kamakura. About half a year later, Akira suddenly lost his wife to influenza. At the same time, by the terms of the Civil Service Retirement Law, he was dismissed from his professorship at the Imperial University. Taking advantage of this, he rented out the house in Sendagimachi and settled down to a leisurely life in the dilapidated cottage in Setagaya, which up to now had been kept as a sort of country house.

Until about ten years before, Akira's father, Genzai,

had lived in retirement in the Setagaya cottage until his death at eighty. Genzai, a scholar of medicinal herbs who had been employed in the herb gardens of the Tokugawa Shogunate at Komaba, had also written books and was well known among his fellow specialists. Often urged after the Meiji Restoration to serve the new government, he had held true to his principles and passed the remainder of his life here at this country retreat. All the trees and plants that flourished today in the garden were the mementos of Genzai.

At first entering the academy of Nakamura Keiu, Akira had completed his studies under Sato Makiyama and Shinobu Joken. Immediately upon graduation from the Imperial University, he'd been engaged as an assistant instructor there. For approximately thirty years, until his retirement, he'd taught a course in Chinese composition. Evidently there was something in him deeply sensitive to the times, however, for he usually advised his students that in today's world the study of a dead way of writing was the apex of foolishness. Deprecating his specialty as something fit only for the dilettante, even when asked for his opinion he would smilingly refuse. Not associating much with his colleagues, he followed his own bent, mainly doing research in Taoism. Although he had written numerous articles, he hadn't published any of them. When he'd learned that his son Susumu was having an affair with a married woman and had set up house with her in defiance of the world, Akira had been profoundly indignant. Thinking, however, that it wasn't likely that the young men and women of this modern age would listen to the admonitions of an old man, he'd completely resigned himself. Pretending to know nothing, he had in fact virtually severed relations with Susumu. In the three years since moving to this retirement cottage in Setagaya, he hadn't communicated with him even once. Susumu, for his part, surmising his father's indignation from his ordinary disposition, as a sign of defiance had deliberately let the weeks and months go by without getting in touch with him.

However, when Akira had gone to Kichijoji Temple in Komagome on his wife's death anniversary, he'd come upon a young woman offering flowers at the grave. Completely taken aback by her presence in the narrow, hedged enclosure, he'd responded to the woman's awkward bow by bluntly asking her name. Only then did he realize that she was his son's wife, Tsuruko. Why would a woman who of her own free will had taken up with the likes of the unruly Susumu know the death anniversary of her mother-in-law, so to speak, and pay a grave-visit? The old man did not understand. He even thought that his aged ears had misheard the name. As they walked along the cemetery path, he asked her again, to make sure. That provided the start of a conversation, and after coming out the temple gates they boarded a trolley together. Almost without their knowing it, their conversation went on and on until it was time to separate. Up to now, Akira had habitually thought that the young men and women of today were totally devoid of any moral sense. In his view, the young men were for the most part a gang of unfilial wastrels, and the young women were not much different from animals. More and more mystified by Tsuruko's ladylike speech and demeanor, he thought it even stranger that someone so conscious of the rules of correct behavior should have committed the sin of adultery. Even after he'd gotten home, he continued to exercise his mind mightily on the matter. Suddenly, it occurred to Akira that Tsuruko had broken her vows of constancy only to be deceived by his debauched scoundrel of a son. If that were so, she was truly to be pitied. Somehow feeling that as a parent he had no excuses to offer, when Akira afterward met Tsuruko by chance at the Shinjuku railway station, he'd gone up to her of his own accord. And so, at some point or another Tsuruko had been given the entree of the house in Setagaya. But, from a sort of mutual reserve, the two did not touch on her relationship with Susumu. The matter remained as it was, without questions asked or statements made. As for financial matters, Susumu had gone on to make enormous sums of money, and the old man's frugal way of life was such that even his pension was too much for him. So that there was no occasion for either him or Tsuruko to discuss household expenses.

Although there was a man who came in to look after the garden and an old woman who did the household chores, Tsuruko had seen that Akira seemed to lack for proper meals, clean clothing, and attentions to his person. Unobtrusively, she did for him whatever she noticed needed doing. If she had said openly that she was going to take care of him, Akira would certainly have answered that it wasn't necessary. Also, there was an elder daughter in the Kiyooka family, who had married a doctor. Fearful of what this lady might think, Tsuruko did everything in a discreet manner so as not to attract her observation. As the days and months went by, Tsuruko's state of mind and feelings naturally became clear to the old man. Pitying her more and more, he could not help but secretly admire her as a person too good for the likes of his son Susumu.

Holding his empty teacup on his knee, the old man said: "I was thinking of visiting your family soon and having a talk with them. But when you get old, putting on formal clothes becomes a nuisance. But it would be impolite not to dress up for a first visit. I'm waiting for a good opportunity. But you will come to see me, won't you, even afterward?"

"Yes. Things will be the same. If it were just my brother, I wouldn't hesitate, but there's also your daughter to consider."

"That may be so."

"At any rate, it's surely I who have been in the wrong. That's why I don't hold anything against anyone."

"It's splendid of you to feel that way." As the old man spoke, a big horsefly alighted on a copybook of stone rubbings of ancient handwriting specimens that had been set out to air. Getting to his feet and chasing the fly away, Akira went on: "One should never be afraid to correct a mistake. The errors of youth cannot be helped. The good or evil of a person comes out in old age."

Tsuruko started to say something but, fearful that despite herself her voice might tremble, remained silent with her head bowed. Her heart suddenly was full, and she felt her eyes grow moist. Luckily, just then, she heard a voice in the kitchen. Making that her opportunity to escape, she hastily got to her feet. The old man, looking in the direction the fly had gone, said: "It's probably either the sake dealer or the postman. Please don't bother yourself." He began to leisurely fold up the pages of the copybook.

Tsuruko, determined not to show her tears, had gone around to the kitchen; sure enough it was the man from the sake dealer's come to deliver a keg of soy. In the kitchen entryway, shaded by a grape arbor, the sunlight fell softly. The breeze that came blowing from the bamboo grove was so bracing it was chilly. The old woman had evidently tidied up the maid's room before leaving. Even the ashes in the brazier had been neatly smoothed out. After the man from the sake dealer's had left, and there seemed to be nobody around, the tears that Tsuruko had held back all at once overflowed. Hastily, she wiped them away with a handkerchief. The old man knew nothing about it, but she and Susumu were a married couple in name only these days. It was no time to be considering whether or not to enter her name in the family register. Susumu had left the house the day before yesterday and probably would not be back by tonight, even. These past two or three years, on the pretext of preparing a manuscript, it had become customary for him to stay away from home as long as he pleased. He would probably be back in two or three days. With things as they were, however, although he would surely not refuse to enter her name in the family register as his legal wife, it was clear without his saying so that it would give him no great pleasure. He might even act as if he were being put upon. Tsuruko, while thinking how grateful she was for Akira's kindness, could not but feel tearful at her inability to accept it.

The love life of Tsuruko and Susumu had lasted barely a year, while they were renting a house in Kamakura. Then Susumu, at a single bound, became the darling of the literary world and started making money hand over fist from his pulp fiction. Not only did he immediately buy a house for a movie actress called Sugihara Suzuko, but he took to going on endless geisha sprees. After Suzuko had discarded him in favor of legal marriage to a fellow actor, Susumu promptly consoled himself by making some cafe waitress his concubine. Although thoroughly disgusted with him, rather than a passion of jealousy

Tsuruko had come to feel a bottomless sadness of despair over her husband's character. Since her girls' school days, Tsuruko had been tutored in language and etiquette by an old French lady and had studied classic literature and calligraphy under a certain Japanese scholar. The discipline and charm of such pursuits had proved her undoing when she married into the prosaic household of a professional soldier. Not only had life in such a household proved unendurable, but even toward the writer Kiyooka Susumu, the man she had chosen for herself, she'd been unable for long to have feelings of affection and respect. When she compared the Susumu of the past when they'd been introduced to each other at a church in Karuizawa and the present Susumu, who was regarded as a great master of popular fiction, she could only think they were completely different people. Susumu five years ago had been an honest, unknown writer true to his serious literary aspirations. As for Susumu today, who could say what he was? Without the least appearance of intellectual anguish, he seemed on the contrary to be endlessly, nervously keeping his eye fixed on fashions and fads. In his diligent money-grubbing, he might well be described as a combination impresario and speculator. When one examined his serialized newspaper fiction, it was simply a rehash in current colloquial language of the banal stories and romances of yesteryear. Surely even the mildly literate housewives it was aimed at must find such trash virtually unreadable. When she had read the story that Susumu had begun to publish in a ladies' magazine from the end of the previous year, Tsuruko had suddenly been reminded of Rokuju-en's *Tales of Hida no Takumi*. She also recalled, as if in a dream, how a professor whose lectures on *The Tale of Genji* she'd attended as a student had been wont to observe that the literary men of the Edo period were infinitely superior to today's writers. Susumu's cronies, who had the run of the house, in their manner of speech and demeanor were all as alike as brothers. When two or three of them were gathered together, they immediately began swilling Western liquor, sitting tailor-style or sprawled out on their sides, and speaking in raucous voices as if they were having a quarrel. When one listened to find out what they were talking about, it was nothing but horse-racing bets, mah-jongg wagers, vicious slander of friends, the vicissitudes of the publishing world, manuscript fees, and absolutely obscene anecdotes about women.

Tsuruko had decided any number of times to leave Susumu's house at the first good opportunity. Since she was no longer welcome at her elder brother's house, she was relying on the money that he'd given her at the time of their estrangement. About half of it was still in the bank. Even prepared if necessary to take a room and find work in an office, Tsuruko had completed her plans and was waiting for the final break to occur. But although she certainly had no fears of a request for alimony from Susumu, she continued to say nothing, coldly honoring her husband in all respects as a proper wife should. As time went by, it became impossible for her to abruptly bring up the matter. And so she had failed to speak to this day. Overwhelmed by these and other sad thoughts, Tsuruko, her handkerchief held between her lips, leaned against the kitchen housepost and listened absentmindedly to the buzz of horseflies in the grape arbor.

Suddenly, there was a sound of footsteps. Caught by surprise, Tsuruko hastily tried to put herself to rights. But the vestiges of tears in the corners of her eyes and the sad pallor of her face were not so easily effaced.

The old man, thinking when Tsuruko had gone to the kitchen and not come back that perhaps it was a trouble-some peddler, had casually stepped around to see how things were.

"Tsuruko, you're not feeling well, are you? Would you like to lie down for a while?"

"No. I'm all right." Despite her words, Tsuruko felt at a loss where to put herself. She sat as if glued to the wooden floor.

"Your color's not good." The old man seemed to have guessed what the matter was. "Whatever I hear from other people I never repeat. In the old days, there was a sage called Hosoi Heishu. Whenever he found a letter belonging to somebody else, he would burn it on the spot. You needn't worry."

Tsuruko, wanting now to confide everything in her heart to this good old man, drew herself close to his feet as if to cling to him. "There's something I want to tell you. Except for you, Father, even though I want to, there's no one I can talk to."

"Hm. I'm listening. I've been thinking that you didn't look yourself at all." Noticing that the glass door of the kitchen had been left wide open by the man from the sake shop, Akira reached out and slid it shut.

"Father, that talk you said you were going to have. It's very kind of you, but I don't think it would come to anything." Tsuruko sniffed back her tears.

"Is that so? Your home life is not going well, is it? What a nuisance. What are your thoughts? Is there no hope for the future?"

"There's nothing in particular going on right now, but even if I were entered in your family register, I would be a wife in name only. There's no telling what may happen.

I've even thought it might be better just to leave things as they are. I'm sorry to be talking about myself this way."

"No, I understand now. It's too bad to speak ill of Susumu to you, but this sort of thing isn't limited to Susumu. Even if you explained what proper conduct was to the young people who play around with literature these days, it's not likely they would understand. I've been a teacher for many years, and I know what I'm talking about. If there were any hope for Susumu, I would call him in and try reasoning with him, but he's just no good. I've resigned myself to it."

"Even when I've said something, it's been awkward . . ."

"That's why even now, as I say, I'm not speaking to him. But if we leave things as they are, your future will be difficult. I'm sorry about that."

"There's no need to be. Whatever happens, I'm no longer young, and so I don't worry that much about the future. And it's not impossible that Susumu may come to have better feelings in the end."

"Hm. Hm." Still standing, arms folded, the old man let out a sigh. Then, hearing a sound from the direction of the back door, he said: "That seems to be Densuke. Let's talk over there."

All but taking her by the hand, the old man hurried Tsuruko out of the kitchen.

SIX

ALTHOUGH it was raining, it was only a drizzle and there was no wind. In the early rainy season sky, the clouds were beginning to break up. At seven o'clock, it was still fairly light. A car pulled up to the gates of the Noda geisha house in Fujimi-cho, and three men got out. One was a big-mouthed, balding man of fifty or so called Komada Hirokichi, who was Kiyooka's literary agent. His companions, one past forty, the other about thirty, clad in business suits and wearing glasses, were recognizable at a glance as newspapermen. Komada, leading the way, slid open the lattice door. Joshing with the maids as they took off their shoes, the three charged upstairs into a large sitting room at the front of the house. Evidently arrangements had been made earlier by telephone, since a smoking set and sitting cushion were in readiness for each guest. The scent of incense hung in the air of the room.

"The bathwater is ready." Shortly after this greeting by the maid, the ripely mature senior geisha, a woman of thirty or so who in this neighborhood would be called "big sister boss," and a geisha of about twenty made their appearance. They began setting out on the table the dishes of food the maid had brought upstairs.

Since the current story by Kiyooka in the *Maruen* newspaper was due to conclude in two weeks, Komada had prudently entered into negotiations with another newspaper for the sale of the next manuscript. Having secretly paid off the managing editor, he was now regaling two of the latter's subordinates at the geisha house.

71

"The sensei will be here presently. He won't mind, so let's start in." Handing a sake cup to the older reporter, Komada removed the lid from a bowl of soup.

"Drinking is just not one of my strong points." Having the geisha pour for him, the older reporter added: "I'm like a geisha who can't play the samisen."

"I'm surprised at you. Popular people have to learn how to drink."

"Haven't I seen you somewhere before? I can't quite remember where. Surely not at a cafe?"

"No, you may have. These days, what with geishas becoming waitresses and waitresses turning into geishas, there's no difference anymore."

"It's not unusual for a geisha to become a waitress, but surely not many waitresses become geishas."

"Not so. It happens all the time. Doesn't it, sis?"

"You don't say. There are a lot of them? I'm astonished."

"That's right. There are five or six of us. . . . If you looked, you might find more."

"Isn't there someone here who used to be on the Ginza or thereabouts?"

"That girl who recently came to us from the Tatsumi-ya . . . what was her name . . . ?" Pausing with her half-drunk cup of sake in her hand, the senior geisha knit her brows. "She was on the Ginza, if I'm not mistaken."

"The Shinbashi Meeting Hall," the younger geisha interjected.

"The Shinbashi Meeting Hall? Is that where she was? About when, was it?"

The younger reporter, who had said nothing up to now, abruptly pushed back the table. Komada looked over his shoulder at the maid.

"Call that geisha. What did you say her name was?"

"Tatsuchiyo of the Tatsumi-ya." The younger geisha having given the name, the maid started to get to her feet. Just then, a voice called up from downstairs: "O-Hana-san. The guest has come."

"It's probably the sensei." Glancing toward the paper door, Komada had no sooner moved aside slightly than there was a sound of footsteps on the ladder-stairs. A panama in one hand and still wearing his gray serge Inverness cape, Kiyooka Susumu was among them.

"Sorry to be late." Handing his hat and cape to the older geisha, and tying the sash of his single-layer iron-blue haori, which he wore over an unlined kimono of striped crepe, Kiyooka seated himself in an empty place at the table, where small dishes of food and chopsticks had been set out. Apparently already acquainted with the older reporter, he was introduced to the younger one. An exchange of cards across the table began immediately. The maid, bringing the geisha's answer along with additional bottles of sake, announced: "Tatsuchiyo will come up in a little while."

"Everybody. Won't you have some more?" Receiving the tray of bottles, the senior geisha continued: "You. Won't you have one?"

"Seems like a very dull party." Having himself served, Kiyooka looked around at Komada. "Are there any others coming?"

"At present, we're still in the process of selection. You don't know of anyone else? There are waitress-geishas, so there are probably ex-dancers and ex-actresses also. Anyway, if we're going to call, someone different would be good."

"He has strange tastes, this one."

"We had an unusual girl here until recently. Who would be good, now?"

"Sis. That girl at the Paulownia Blossom House. Isn't there a lot of talk about her?"

"You mean Kyoyo-san." The senior geisha slapped her knee. "She's better than a dancer. She can stand on her head."

"She's probably a fright to look at, though."

"No, she's beautiful, and sexy. She's the busiest person in this neighborhood."

"You're giving her a terrific buildup. I'll have a little more. Anyway, call her, call her." Komada, who seemed to be getting slightly drunk, was lively. But Kiyooka, hearing the name of Kyoyo of the Paulownia Blossom House, was unpleasantly reminded of that incident late the previous summer. Since he could not veto the suggestion, however, he assumed a noncommittal expression.

The senior geisha, seeking to add interest to the conversation, said: "If I were three or four years younger, I'd give up being a geisha and launch out on the Ginza myself. Because waitresses are at least respectable types on the surface. No matter what they do, they can gloss it over. That's what I think. The house right next door to mine is an assignation house. Waitresses bring all sorts of customers there. The houses are close together, so if you put your head out the window there's just a paper door between you and the people next door. You can hear everything they say. There's a tall, slender girl, better dressed than a geisha. She must be from a fashionable cafe on the Ginza. She always comes early in the morning. Sometimes, she even comes before nine o'clock. Then, she leaves at around noon. I'm just barely awake by nine or ten. Right now, they're not keeping any girls there. It's dead quiet. It makes me strain my ears to hear something."

Kiyooka silently had himself served more sake by the young geisha. The two reporters, apparently fascinated by this account, egged on the senior geisha. "Yes, and then? And then?" Getting into the spirit of the thing, the geisha went on: "Sometimes the clients are different. But they're always saying 'Kimi-san, Kimi-san,' so there must be a girl who goes there called Kimiko or Kimiyo. She's really extraordinary. There was something that happened—when was it?—that truly astonished me."

Kiyooka glanced up sharply at the reporters' faces. Komada, as an older, more experienced man, soon noticed the danger. Worried that it was Kimie of the Don Juan who was the subject of the geisha's discourse, he covertly observed the reporters. But both of them seemed to be remarkably unconversant with the world of the Ginza cafes. Without any particular sign of awareness, one of them asked: "What was it that astonished you? Was she more passionate than a geisha?"

"Of course. Just listen. You'll hardly believe this, but . . ."

Komada, to stop the conversation from going any further, adroitly cut in. "Hey, what's happened to that geisha you called before? Go downstairs and tell her to come up."

"Yes." The younger geisha got to her feet. Komada then added: "I'll have some rice soon."

"I'll join you." The younger reporter, who hadn't had anything to drink, chimed in. What with the serving of the rice and the brewing of fresh green tea, the geisha's story was broken off. Just then, the woman called Tatsu-chiyo knelt formally outside the opened paper door.

Her age was about twenty. The ribbons of raw silk in her low Shimada coiffure were cut long, and the skirts of her light purple kimono with a "flying pattern" trailed on the floor. Her large, firm-bodied figure suggested the prostitute rather than the geisha.

"Are you the one who was on the Ginza?"

"Yes. I am." With a rather complacent air, Tatsuchiyo went on: "Perhaps I've seen you there. Anyway, I'm awfully shortsighted. I'm always not recognizing people. They think I'm being rude."

Seemingly much annoyed at the way Tatsuchiyo prattled on without so much as a glance in her direction, the senior geisha glared at her out of the corner of her eye. Apparently noticing nothing, Tatsuchiyo drank off one after the other two cups of sake poured for her by the younger reporter and returned the cup to him. "Since coming here, I haven't been back to the Ginza even once. It must have changed. What are the liveliest cafes nowadays?"

"Where were you before? The Columbia?"

"Oh, excuse me. I was at the Shinbashi Meeting Hall."

"Why did you become a geisha? Because you were living too fast and came under surveillance?"

"You say that, but actually cafes are rather respectable. Because we're in the cafe from noon until midnight."

"What do you do after midnight?"

"After midnight? Doesn't everybody go to bed? One can't stay up all night, can one? Eh, you."

Just then, a petite geisha of twenty-two or -three, her hair also done in a low Shimada coiffure, and a tall geisha of eighteen or nineteen, wearing the latest hairdo, made their entrance, seating themselves at the bottom of the table. Kiyooka needed no reminder that the small woman was Kyoyo. He wasn't likely to forget for the rest of his life that night when he shadowed Kimie from the precincts of the Hachiman Shrine in Ichigaya. Thinking it better not to be recognized by Kyoyo, on his two or three visits to this neighborhood since then he had taken care not to encounter her. Feigning casualness, he turned away and blew out smoke from his cigarette. Komada, finishing his rice, got up and went out into the corridor.

"Komada-san. Just a moment." The maid drew him toward the back stairs. "O-Kita-san. Sis. It already will cost a lot, so send the other one back."

"What about the two that came last? Are they all right?" Komada glanced at his watch.

"Kikuyo is a bit expensive, but . . ."

"If that's so, send her back too. I won't be needing one, so it's all right if there are just three."

"Well then, Kyoyo-san, Tatsuchiyo-san, and Matsuyo-san." The maid said the names over for emphasis. "How shall we do this, now?"

Since the maid seemed to be at a loss how to assign the girls, Komada decided to slip behind the front desk on his way back from the privy and call Kiyooka downstairs, leaving the two reporters to choose the girls they wanted.

"I'll do that, then."

When the maid went back inside to send the senior geisha away, the younger reporter, the ex-waitress Tatsuchiyo on his knee, was sitting at the window and looking out as he sang some popular song. Leaving him so, the maid whispered to the older reporter. Kiyooka, surmising what was up, on the pretext of going to the privy and also to look for Komada, unobtrusively left the room and went down the backstairs. By the time he'd come back up, neither reporter was to be seen. The maid, picking

up their briefcases and discarded jackets, as the latter was
about to leave was saying to Kyoyo: "It's on the third
floor—right at the end of the hall." Pretending not to
listen, Kiyooka sat down on the windowsill. The tall,
stylish geisha, apparently thinking from the look of things
that Kiyooka was her customer, saying: "It's cleared up
already," seated herself beside him.

At some time or other, the rain had stopped. Along
the straight, narrow street lined on both sides with geisha
houses, the sound of clogs going back and forth grew
slightly more frequent. From a distant corner, there came
the refrain of a popular song, accompanied on a violin,
by a street singer.

"That O-Kita who went back just now. Where is her
house? In Fujimi-cho?" Kiyooka asked, as of some un-
important matter. Actually, he was bothered by the matter of that next-door assignation house the woman had
talked about.

"No. She's way out past Sanban-cho, even . . ."

"Isn't there a girls' school or something out there?"

"Yes. My own house is right next to O-Kita-san's."

"Is that so? But didn't she say that her house was next
door to an assignation house?"

"Yes. That would be the Chiyoda house. Next door
but one is O-Kita-san's house, and the one on this side is
my house."

"Is that so? That must be the house, then. That makes
side-by-side assignation houses, doesn't it?"

"It's strange, somehow."

"I owe them a visit, so I've been thinking I'd go there
soon. But I don't know how things are there."

"Out there the Chiyoda house is the only place where
you can sleep with the girls. It's the farthest out of the
licensed quarters."

During the Rains

The maid, coming down from the third floor, welcomed Kiyooka. Kiyooka, however, not particularly attracted by the geisha, merely said: "What happened to Komada? I've got a little business with him. He can't have gone back yet."

"He was at the desk talking with the proprietor a little while ago. I'll go and see."

As the maid was leaving, Komada, stuffing a big billfold into a pocket of his jacket, came up the front stairs. If it was on business, Komada was willing to go to an assignation house, a cafe, or whatever, but he only rarely ordered a woman. Since he'd been working in the business department of his newspaper, he had dabbled in real estate and the stock market. He was rumored to be a rather wealthy man by now. Despite that, he still lived in a little house in Yotsuya-Teramachi, up an alley so narrow that not even a rickshaw could enter it. He'd been there since the days before streetcars. In Kiyooka's opinion, Komada was a miser of the old school who would have set fire to his own fingernails if he could save money thereby.

"Komada. If you're going back, I'll leave with you. It's still early, so probably we can catch a trolley."

"Are you going on to the Ginza from here?"

"No. I've already given that up. You know how it is— if she's someone who sees everybody, it damages your reputation. There's something I want to talk to you about. We'll leave when you're ready."

"Well. You really are leaving, then?" The geisha seemed genuinely surprised. Kiyooka, however, without looking at her, drew toward him the bellrope that hung on the post by the window and pressed the button.

Komada, as he was going down the stairs with Kiyooka, as if he'd suddenly remembered something, turned around toward the maid, who was seeing them

79

off. "Hey, you. If they stay overnight, send the geishas back in the morning."

"That's already taken care of."

"I don't think there was anything else. Give me some matches, and we'll be off." Even while putting on his shoes, Komada made sure to get his money's worth.

"Thank you very much. Please come again soon." Sliding open the lattice door, the two men stepped outside. The moon had come out. It was a typical summer evening in the licensed quarters. In the alleys, the yukatas of the women going back and forth caught the eye.

"Komada, you'll go with me to Akasaka, won't you?"

"So that's where you're going these days?"

"Because I'm already tired of the cafes. Geishas are the best after all. I've been thinking of finding some nice lively geisha and setting her up."

"Setting her up? You mean buying out her contract? You'll have to think about it carefully."

"I knew you'd say that, if I talked it over with you."

"You'd probably do better not laying out a round sum of money. That goes for buying out the contract, too. If she thinks there's a chance of your marrying her, she'll play fair and square with you. But if not, something unpleasant is bound to happen, and you'll have to let her go anyway."

"But even I don't know what the future may hold. I might even become single again . . ."

"Is that so? Stormy weather ahead for you, in that case."

"No, it's not as bad as all that. It's just that—I don't know why, but whenever I go home I get intolerably depressed."

Thinking he would like to tell Komada the full story of his domestic arrangements, to answer all questions,

Kiyooka walked along, mulling over how and where to begin. All of a sudden, they were at the Fujimi-cho trolley stop. In the first place, Kiyooka had never really meant to make Tsuruko his legal wife. It had been his intention merely to enjoy occasional secret trysts with her. But the woman had been extraordinarily in earnest. The affair had turned unexpectedly serious, and he hadn't known what to do. Luckily for him, he learned that she had received a sum of money from her elder brother. With it, he had rented a house in Kamakura and lived together with her. Of course, he was quite aware that Tsuruko's beauty and character would place her above reproach as his wife. As time passed, however, thanks to his own immoral life Kiyooka had begun to feel somehow ashamed of himself. Knowing that he had to be careful about telling even a single off-color joke, he felt unbearably cramped. Unless he went at least once a day to a cafe or an assignation house and drank and had silly conversations with the waitresses or geishas, he felt unendurably lonely. If the waitress Kimie had been just a little more forthcoming, Kiyooka would have liked to set her up immediately with her own bar or cafe. But, knowing how unreliable Kimie was, he'd changed his mind and was now thinking of setting up a geisha as soon as he found the right one. He'd been hoping to elicit Komada's opinion on the matter. But Komada, seeing the trolley coming, shifting his grip on his briefcase, all but leaped aboard with an agility remarkable for his years. Immediately losing interest, Kiyooka said: "I'll say good-bye, then. There's someplace I have to go."

"Tomorrow. I'll be at the office in the afternoon. If there's something you want to talk about, give me a ring." Komada answered from the trolley as it moved off.

Kiyooka looked at his pocket watch. It was ten o'clock. Since it was not that late, now would be a good time to go home. Late-night reveler that he was, though, Kiyooka felt somehow dissatisfied. He could not force his steps in a homeward direction until he'd visited one other place somewhere. But at this hour, he could not just stroll into someplace like the Don Juan on the Ginza, which would be jammed with customers and where one of the waitresses was his mistress. Fearful also of being harassed by the rascals and delinquent literary types who frequented the eating and drinking shops around the Ginza, he had no wish to see Kimie laughing and carrying on with some drunken customer. The place to go to was that assignation house in Akasaka he'd visited occasionally of late. But the geisha there that he had his eye on, although he'd already engaged her five or six times, did not seem overly amenable to his proposition. When he thought that even tonight the matter would not be settled, Kiyooka felt irritated even before he'd made his visit. His anger, however, when he had thought it over, did not spring from the geisha's refusal to do his will. The cause, as always, arose from his feelings of indignation toward Kimie. If Kimie had only done what he wanted her to, he would not have had to make a fool of himself getting rejected by the geisha. The desire for revenge, which for a while he had put aside, once again welled up hotly in him. What aroused Kiyooka's wrath more than anything else was how Kimie spent her days in apparent pleasure without a care in the world. Next was the fact that she didn't appear particularly overjoyed to have a famous writer as her lover. Even if he broke off the relationship, it seemed as if she would feel no especial regret or anything much at all. If the relationship ended, Kimie would no doubt take advantage of that to find a new lover and go on living in the same empty-headed, frivolous manner as before. There was no one more difficult to manage than a woman without either ambition or desire for money, who simply wanted to live out her lewd, indolent existence. To make such a woman suffer, the only way might be to inflict physical pain upon her. And yet, since one could not do such things as cut off all her hair or slash her face, one could only wait for her to contract some serious illness that would confine her to bed for two or three months. Mulling over such matters, following his feet wherever they led him, Kiyooka abruptly looked around him. This brilliantly illuminated place—it was the entrance of the Ichigaya railway station. Diagonally opposite, the low houses of the neighborhoods on the far side of the Moat were visible. Under the early rainy season sky that was beginning to cloud over in impenetrable darkness, an advertisement for Jintan Pills flashing on and off caught Kiyooka's eye.

Kimie's house was up the alley where that sign was flashing on and off. Not only had he not seen her for nearly three days, from the day before yesterday until tonight, but mindful of that story he'd heard earlier from the geisha in Fujimi-cho, Kiyooka decided the best thing was to secretly reconnoiter the place. Going along by the Moat, he turned in at the usual alley.

The lights in the windows of the sake shop and the drugstore on the corner illuminated every nook and cranny of the narrow alley so clearly that one could make out the faces of passers-by. For about a year now, Kiyooka had been coming here every four or five days. Thinking he was certain to be recognized by the shopclerks, he pulled down his hat brim deeply over his eyes and hurried past. Ahead of him, the sweets shop and the tobacconist's were still open. Along there, though, the lights were very dim, and nobody was standing around in front of the shops. The fish shop at the corner of Kimie's alley had already closed. Looking around him, Kiyooka was just about ready to enter the dark alley when he abruptly encountered the old woman who was Kimie's landlady. Pretending not to recognize her, he tried to slip past her in the darkness. But the sharp-eyed old woman called out: "Why, it's the sensei. We almost walked right by each other. What a lucky encounter. There have been burglaries, so I'd locked up and was on my way to the bathhouse. Is O-Kimi-san coming back early tonight?"

"No. I had a little business in Ichigaya, so I thought I'd drop by. I can't wait until she gets back. Please don't tell her I was here tonight. I've been slightly worried about her."

"Well then, just come in for a cup of tea."

"But weren't you on your way to the bathhouse, Auntie?"

"Oh come now, you. There's no great hurry about that."

Since he could not simply shake her off and go on his way, Kiyooka, as invited, entered the downstairs sitting room where the old woman slept and lived, and sat down at the long brazier. It was the same sort of six-mat room as the one upstairs. Although the walls and ceiling were sooty, and there were even floorboards missing, it was kept clean and neat down to the last nook and corner. All the tears in the paper doors had been patched. Had there been a tenant available, even this room could have been rented out. In the ornamental alcove, looking as if it had hung there forever, there was a picture scroll of Mari-

shiten* or some such deity. Atop an old utility chest that
had faded to the hue of persimmon paper, a small household shrine had been set up. Over the long brazier, an iron
teakettle hung in a Yoshiwara holder that had been pol-
ished until it shone. From such utensils and furniture, one
probably could have guessed the old woman's approxi-
mate age. According to the old woman herself, after her
husband, a first lieutenant in the army at the time of the
Russo-Japanese War, had died in battle, she had supported
herself by working as a housemaid or temporary housekeeper and had also done piecework at home. By these
means, she had raised her daughter. The daughter had
had the good fortune to marry a wealthy importer, and
the couple now lived in America. So that the old woman
should want for nothing, they sent her an allowance. According to others, however, although the allowance from
the daughter was real enough, the latter had been the concubine of a foreigner. When she gave birth to a child, she
had been taken away by her lord and master to his own
country. Kiyooka was not only unable to decide which
of these versions was true, but could not make out why
Kimie had rented the second floor of this house in the
first place, and why she didn't move to a nicer house in a
better neighborhood. Despite her claim to have been the
wife of an officer, to judge from her present appearance
and manner of speaking the old woman belonged to a
type frequently to be met with in the back alleys of the
Honjo-Asakusa area. That both her birth and upbringing
had been lowly appeared in the fact that she could barely
read the bill from the sake shop. Her mindless deference
toward anyone with a mustache and wearing Western

*God of War (tr. note).

clothes told one just about all there was to know about
her. It would do no good to ask her what Kimie had been
up to in the intervals between his visits. Not letting his
long-cherished grudge show in his face, with as good-
humored a manner as he could manage, Kiyooka said:
"If I go to the cafe, I run into all sorts of people. It's a
nuisance. That's why even when I pass by at night I try
not to go inside."

"That's wise. When they see a famous person like yourself, people want to start up all sorts of rumors. Oh dear—
it's already eleven o'clock." Listening to the clock in the
house next door chime the hour, the old woman looked
up at the octagonal clock on top of the utility chest.

"Sensei, if you can wait another hour, she'll be back.
Please do wait. I'll put some more coals on the brazier."

"Auntie. It doesn't have to be tonight. I'll come by
in the morning." So saying, Kiyooka slipped his pack of
Shikishimas into his kimono sleeve. But the old woman
had put two and two together. From Kiyooka's hanging around this neighborhood at such an odd hour, and
Kimie's slatternly behavior, which she'd kept an eye on
night and day, she surmised the general situation. Pretending to know nothing, though, she said: "But, sensei,
unless I keep you here, I'll be scolded for it afterward by
Kimie-san."

"If you don't tell her, she won't know anything."

"But somehow I don't feel easy about it. I'll use the
telephone at the sake shop and call her up." Groping about
in the drawer of the brazier, the old woman took out a
scrap of paper on which was written a telephone number.

"Well then, I'll lie down upstairs until you get back.
But she's sure to be back herself by twelve, so there's no
need for you to call." Getting to his feet, Kiyooka added:

"I'll watch over the house, Auntie, so go and have your bath if you like."

When he'd sent the old woman off to the bathhouse, Kiyooka went upstairs. If any secret love letters were lying about, he meant to lay hands on them. The old woman, having often been urgently requested by Kimie to telephone her if anything unexpected came up, decided to make the call at the sake shop or the drugstore on her way to the baths. Tucking away the scrap of paper with its scribbled phone number in her obi, she set out.

WHEN the phonecall came from the old woman, Kimie luckily was drinking with a customer at a table near the phone booth. She went to the phone as soon as she was summoned. But in addition to being rather drunk (it was thirty or forty minutes to closing time), she was prevented by the noise around her from hearing well. She understood that Kiyooka had come to her place, but could not make out a word of the old woman's lengthy explanation. Tonight was not one of the nights Kiyooka was supposed to come, and there had been no advance word from him. Kimie had felt free to make an engagement earlier in the evening to spend the night somewhere with a dancer called Kimura Yoshio, who had recently returned from the West. Then Yata-san, the foreign-car dealer with whom she had been intimate two or three times, had shown up. Also inviting Haruyo and Yuriko, he'd insisted that on their way home Kimie stop off at the newly opened noodle shop on the street in back of the Matsuya Dry Goods Store. If she had another engagement, an hour or half an hour would be fine, Yata had said. Going out for a while, he'd just this minute come back and was treating four or five waitresses to various snacks. At about the same time, the old gentleman called Matsuzaki, who almost never went to cafes and the like, had suddenly appeared. Of course, he explained, he was on his way back from seeing somebody off at Tokyo Station.

At all the cafes on the Ginza, not just the Don Juan,

after ten o'clock, toward closing time, it usually got very crowded all of a sudden. The noise of the constantly playing phonograph, intermittently drowned out by the clamor of voices, mingled with the clatter of plates amid drifting motes of dust and cigarette smoke. To make matters worse, Kimie had a headache. Just when even she had begun to think that maybe she'd had a little too much to drink this evening, three men had descended upon her here at the cafe, and back at her place another one was waiting for her. She was practically at her wit's end. What to do? Why tonight of all nights were circumstances so unfavorable? It was enough to make her envy people in more respectable professions. If she could drink herself into a stupor, the others would take care of her one way or another. With this in mind, Kimie approached old man Matsuzaki's table. "I want to get dead drunk tonight. Buy me an 'auto-car,' please."

"Are you in some kind of trouble? Did you quarrel with one of your customers?" By virtue of his years, Matsuzaki seemed to know at once how things were with Kimie.

"No. That's not it. But . . ."

" 'But'—so it *is* something of that sort."

At a loss for an answer, Kimie was silent. Then, it occurred to her that since this old man had known her from the days before she'd become a waitress and knew everything there was to know about her, it might be well to tell him her problem and ask his advice. Luckily, there was not a single other waitress at the table. Snuggling up to Matsuzaki, Kimie said: "I'm really in a fix tonight. This is the first time circumstances have been so unfavorable."

Matsuzaki, who seemed to have guessed everything instantly from Kimie's manner and way of speaking, replied: "I'm leaving in a few minutes. I just thought I'd drop by and see how things were at the cafe tonight. Let's meet again soon, during the day, when you'll have more time."

"I'm sorry. Please don't be angry with me."

"Of course not. I understand. You've probably got more than one customer on your hands."

"When all is said and done, you're the only one, though. How did you know, Uncle?" Kimie, putting her mouth to Matsuzaki's ear, gave him the lowdown about tonight, not holding back a single detail.

"Can't you suggest some good plan?"

"There are any number of things you can do. It's no problem." Matsuzaki promptly imparted to Kimie his scheme of action. First, on her way back from the cafe, she was to rush one of her customers to an assignation house. Since there would be no question of her staying overnight, after a while, before the man got ready to leave, Kimie could apologize for leaving first, pretend to be hurrying home, and hide in another room. Previously, she would have sent a waitress whom she could trust to the house in Ichigaya to tell the old woman that they had unsuspectingly accepted a ride from a customer only to be taken off by force to an assignation house. While the customer was calling for a geisha and plying them with food and drink, the waitress alone, seeing her opportunity, had escaped. The old woman must come at once to fetch Kimie-san. Undoubtedly, it would be Kiyooka who came to the assignation house. As it would take him more than an hour to get there, Kimie would easily be able to take care of one customer. As for the other customer, with the excuse that she was afraid of being seen, Kimie would send him on ahead to another assignation house. It was too bad, but he would have to sleep by himself

tonight. Of course, he would be very angry, but his longing for Kimie was sure to grow stronger in proportion
to his chagrin. The next day, he would certainly come to
reproach her. If, on that occasion, she gave him his heart's
desire, the result would be more felicitous than if nothing had happened. Stroking his clipped gray mustache,
Matsuzaki smilingly added: "However, to carry off a job
like this, it has to be a place where the people are intelli-
gent and resourceful. Is there some house you're friendly
with that would be suitable?"

"Yes. There is. That place out in Ushigome. I went
there with you two or three times when I was living in
Suwamachi. And these days, there's a place in Sanban-cho
I go to occasionally."

Just then, a waitress came to take Matsuzaki's order.
Kimie, making some irrelevant joke, got up and left the
table. Since there was only half an hour to closing time,
Matsuzaki thought he might find out who Kimie's customers were in the interval. He also felt curious to see
what kind of action Kimie would in fact take. But, thinking that it would be difficult to sit still that long, he
soon paid the bill and left the cafe. On both sides of the
street, the shops had turned off their lights and closed
their doors. What with the rain that had fallen earlier and
the late hour, only a few stand-up eating and drinking
stalls were still open. Along the main thoroughfare of
the Ginza, the wide streets that led off to the right and
left were all deserted as far as the eye could see. Above
was the dark night sky, which loomed with a promise of
more rain, and below the colored lights of the bars and
cafes reflected in the wet surface of the pavement. The
theaters and variety halls had already closed an hour ago.
All the couples strolling about idly at this hour seemed to

be coming or going to or from the cafes. The trolleys that passed by were comparatively empty. Only taxis, with no apparent destination, cruised the intersections.

Matsuzaki, who nowadays came to the Ginza only now and then on business, felt something of the curiosity of the sightseer. Without actually stopping, he loitered at the Owari-cho intersection. As always, when he observed the scene around him, it seemed to him that only now, at this late hour, did the transformation of this district and the trend of the times come home to him. They brought in their wake the memories of half a lifetime.

Matsuzaki, who held a law degree, had at one time been a high official in a government ministry in Kobiki-cho. Implicated in a graft scandal that had shocked the nation, however, he had been tried and sentenced to prison. After his release from prison, however, all was clear sailing. Thanks to his deals, he'd accumulated a private income sufficient to let him enjoy himself for the rest of his life. His children were already grown and on the road to success. When he compared the Ginza that he'd seen every day on his way to the ministry in his own rickshaw from his mansion in Kojimachi for several years, and the present-day scene, changing day by day since the Earthquake, Matsuzaki could not but feel that he was dreaming. The dream did not hold the deep emotion with which a modern Roman thinks of the ancient city of Rome. It implied only the shallow admiration that the spectator at a variety show feels for the dexterity of a juggler. When a city aped the West to the degree that Tokyo did, the spectacle provoked in the observer an astonishment, along with a certain sense of pathos. More than merely from the appearance of the streets, this pathos was felt especially keenly when one thought of the circumstances of the waitresses who had to make their living in this district. Women like Kimie, by nature lacking any sense of feminine decorum and chastity, were doubtless not few among the waitresses. Even though she was a prostitute like them, Kimie was of a totally different kind from the geisha–prostitutes of the past. She was the same type of unlicensed prostitute that flourishes in the cities of the West. The fact that such women had appeared in the streets of Tokyo, if one attributed it to the atmosphere of the period, prompted the reflection that nothing was so surprising as the changes of time. Looking back on his own life, Matsuzaki felt no particular shame as he recalled being hauled into court and being convicted of malversation. Perhaps this also was one of the effects of the atmosphere of the period. More than twenty years had passed since then. Even though this old man who at one time had been so noisily discussed was today having a quiet drink in a Ginza cafe, no one, if they had known of it, would have thought it strange or criticized him. Time had buried the uproar, along with his merits and demerits, in oblivion. That, indeed, one would have to say, was truly like a dream. Toward the world and toward his own career, Matsuzaki felt the same melancholy mixture of resentment and cold contempt. In life, there was neither past nor future, only the pleasures and pains of day-to-day existence. Matsuzaki had come to feel that there was no need to take either praise or censure too much to heart. If that were so, he was bound to consider himself as the most fortunate of human beings. At age sixty, he was in good health. Occasionally, without any fear of what people would think, he put his arm around twenty-year-old waitresses and flirted with them like a young man. Moreover, he felt no shame in doing so. In this alone, his happiness exceeded by far that of royalty. Matsuzaki could not help laughing out loud.

Kimie, as previously arranged, after leaving the cafe met the dancer Kimura Yoshio on the dark river promenade that runs toward Yuraku Bridge. From there, they went by car to the friendly Chiyoda assignation house in Sanban-cho. As instructed to by old man Matsuzaki, Kimie meant to pretend to leave ahead of the customer and hide out in another room, where she would await Kiyooka with an innocent expression on her face. On the way, however, Kimura's conversation revealed that he was a surprisingly sophisticated person. Apparently he thought it a matter of course that a waitress should have two or three lovers. When they'd gone upstairs to the second floor rear of the Chiyoda, Kimie immediately told him about tonight's situation. As she'd expected, Kimura went along with everything.

"If you had told me right away, I wouldn't have had to cause you all this trouble. Please forgive me. I've done the wrong thing. We'll meet some other time, when you're not quite so busy."

As if deliberately urging her on, Kimura helped Kimie with her preparations, even tying her obi for her.

Ever since she had seen Kimura perform in the intermission between movies at the Horaku Theater, Kimie had been stirred up by her usual curiosity. Parting in this manner left her with an unbearably dissatisfied feeling. Kimura's art, to go by articles he had published in newspapers and magazines, was an amalgam of the Russian dance since Nijinsky and Chinese theatrical dance, in short a mixture of East and West. The linear beauty of the movements of the male and female body, Kimura claimed, was far superior to the stationary effect of sculpture and the plastic arts. Furthermore, it was more profound than the intuitive, suggestive power of music. To the waitress Kimie, however, this sort of aesthetic discussion was all one. When she'd seen naked young men and women cavorting about the stage, striking various poses and occasionally embracing each other in front of a large audience, she'd wondered what it would be like to meet the man who made his living from that sort of show. There was no difference between her feeling and that of the shameless geisha who patronizes a sumo wrestler or the girl student who develops a crush on a baseball player.

"Sensei, it's already late, so you won't go home, will you? You'll go to some other place. I'm jealous."

"But your patron is coming. You don't have any choice, do you? I'm going straight home. If you don't believe me, try calling me up." Handing her his card, Kimura added: "Kimie-san, please let's meet again."

"Yes, let's. Please. Somehow I have the feeling I've done something really unforgivable. I don't want to send you away." As usual, Kimie was unable to repress her interest in a new man. Leaning against the knee of Kimura, who had already begun his preparations for departure, she took hold of his hand.

After a while, saying that she would engage a car for his return, Kimie stepped out into the corridor to call the maid. Asking the time, she was told that it had just now struck two. The customer called Kiyooka had not yet appeared, nor had there been a phonecall. The car arrived, and the dancer Kimura took his leave. The writer Kiyooka, however, still hadn't shown up. It was now past two-thirty. When the cafe closed, Kimie had sent a fellow waitress called Ruriko to Ichigaya with her story. From her days as an assistant in a Western-style hairdressing salon, Ruriko had the entree of many assignation houses. She was not likely to make a mistake in an affair of this kind. Perhaps Kiyooka, without getting Ruriko's message, had gone home early in a rage. Kimie felt more and more regretful, unbearably so, at having sent Kimura away. When she looked at his card, which she had slipped inside her obi, it had the phone number of his residence, the Showa Apartments. With the sudden reckless idea of calling him, Kimie started down the backstairs. Just then, from the front, there was the sound of somebody's arrival. Thinking it must be Kiyooka, Kimie strained her ears. But as she listened to the voice of the visitor as he came upstairs to the second floor front, Kimie realized that it was not Kiyooka. It seemed to be the untimely Yata. At the cafe, although urgently invited, she had told him that she had a prior engagement and could not go to the back-street noodle shop with him. Instead, she'd said, if it were a little later she would go anywhere he liked. Giving him the name of an assignation house, she'd sent him on ahead with the lie that she would meet him there later.

Yata, for his part, had taken Kimie at her word. Going to the assignation house, the one behind the Kagura Slope where he'd taken Kimie the first night, he waited patiently until after two o'clock. There had not even been a phone-call. Guessing what was up, Yata remembered the Chiyoda house in Sanban-cho, where Kimie had taken him ten days ago on her way to work. If she was there, he would cause a commotion and make a nuisance of himself by way of revenge. It was with this in mind that Yata had suddenly arrived at the Chiyoda. When he knocked at the gate, the maid came out to slide open the rain shutters. "Is

Kimie-san here?" To this crafty inquiry, the maid, taking
it for granted that Yata was the customer Kimie had been
waiting for, replied: "The lady has been waiting for ever
so long. You men are really inconsiderate." Suffocated by
his own cigarette smoke, Yata could say nothing. Obediently going upstairs, he sat down tailor-style in front
of the ornamental alcove. Not even taking his hat off, he
looked around the room dubiously.

Informed of the situation by the maid at the foot of
the backstairs, Kimie decided that she would have to
make the best of things. Immediately going back upstairs,
she slid open the opaque paper door. "Ya-san, this is too
much." Her voice sharp, Kimie upbraided him.

Yata, still not over his surprise at the maid's reply,
and speechless at Kimie's extraordinary attitude, merely
blinked at her.

"I was thinking of going back." Primly seating herself,
Kimie looked down at the mat.

"What on earth is going on?" Seeming to notice it for
the first time, Yata took off his hat. "Somehow I'm all up
in the air."

Kimie, her eyes lowered, silently toyed with a handkerchief in her lap. Bringing some freshly brewed tea, the
maid entered the room. "You've truly had a long wait,
miss. Shall I bring some sake?"

"It's already too late," Kimie said, her voice curiously
low and melancholy. "I'm terribly sorry to have made
you stay up so long."

"I'm used to late hours. If that will be all . . ." Taking
Yata's hat and light summer overcoat, the maid got to her
feet. There was no chance for Yata to say anything. The
maid leading the way, he wordlessly entered the four-
and-a-half-mat room at the rear of the second floor, all

unaware that it was the same room in which the dancer had been entertained.

Although hearing in her sleep the sound of the brief downpour that came at daybreak of the short summer night, Kimie dozed for a while longer. Suddenly, at the shrill voice of a woman in the alley, exclaiming right under her window how hot it had gotten, and the staccato clip-clop of clogs as someone ran by, she opened her eyes. In the eaves, sparrows were singing. From not far away, there was the sound of someone practicing on the samisen. From the front of the house, along with the sounds of housecleaning and wooden and paper doors being slid open and shut, there were footsteps from the neighbor's as someone went up to the roof to hang out the laundry. The rain had gone away, and the sun was glittering in a clear sky. Inside the room, its windows and doors all closed and the light bulb still on from last evening, the stuffy heat was even more oppressive. Her head aching from the musty odor of sleep, despite her experience of such evenings, Kimie crawled off the bedding and began opening the rain shutters.

"Leave it. I'll do it. It really has gotten hot." Yata's humor had taken a turn for the better during the night.

"Oh, my. Just try touching this." Taking off her long underwear of bleached cotton with a delicate red collar, Kimie, on all fours, reached out her arm toward the window to let the garment dry in the breeze. Observing her pose, Yata commented: "You're a lot more charming than the likes of the Kimura Dancers."

"How do you mean, charming?"

"I'm referring to your physical charms."

Thinking what a good saying that was about ignorance

and bliss, Kimie stifled a desire to laugh. "Ya-san, I'll bet you know somebody in that troupe. They all have good figures. Even a woman thinks that, looking at them. For a man, it must be seventh heaven."

"It's not like that at all. They're fine as long as they're on the stage. Face to face, they're not worth talking about. Dancers and models don't know how to do anything except take their clothes off. Conversationally, they're duds. You've spoiled me for other women, Kimie-san."

"Ya-san, you mustn't make fun of others like that."

His face suddenly serious, Yata was about to say something. Just then, from outside the room, the maid inquired: "Are you already up? The bathwater is ready."

"It's already ten o'clock." Drawing his wristwatch to him from beside the pillow, Yata said: "I've got to drop over to the office on a little business. But, Kimie-san, are you on the late shift today?"

"Today, I'm on from three o'clock. It's too hot to go back to my place, so I'll rest up here until then. Why don't you do the same?"

"Hm. I'd like to, but . . ." Yata thought it over for a moment. "Well, anyway, let's have our bath."

Calling his showroom, Yata was informed that something had arisen which absolutely required his presence. Not even having any breakfast, he took his leave of Kimie and hurried off. By now, it was getting toward noon. Still puzzled as to what had become of Kiyooka, Kimie phoned the fish dealer's in front of her place, on whom she usually relied in such matters, and had them call the old woman to the phone. She was told that last night her friend the waitress had come, and the sensei had gone out together with her. That was all. Perhaps Kiyooka and Ruriko had struck up an amorous acquaintance, Kimie surmised. If so, that would explain his not having shown up here. However, that was just a thought of hers, and Kimie felt no inclination to exercise herself about it. Since leaving home in the fall of her seventeenth year and coming to Tokyo four years ago, Kimie had slept with so many men that she'd lost count. And yet, Kimie had never sought the kind of love that is described in novels. That was why she had never experienced the emotion called jealousy. Rather than have one man deeply fall for her, and because of that enduring his angers and grudges, getting into troublesome entanglements and being bound to him because she had taken his money, Kimie thought it best to frolic on the spot, as the spirit moved her and to her heart's content with anyone who presented himself, be he young or old, handsome or ugly. That way there was no bad aftertaste. From the end of her seventeenth year down to this very day in her twentieth year, Kimie had been pursued by the insatiable demands of such frivolity. She had not had the leisure to consider deeply what manner of thing the true emotion of serious love might be. It was not that (every once in a very long while) Kimie did not sleep by herself in her second-floor rented room, but her principal desire on such nights was to catch up on her chronic lack of sleep. Also, she would begin to imagine the new pleasures that would naturally follow once she'd recovered from her fatigue. Any other subject, no matter how serious, as she dropped off to sleep, became dim and insubstantial, as if she were dreaming. To Kimie, nothing was so enjoyable as that mixture of feelings and sensations at the moment of waking, as she tried to make out which was reality and which a dream.

Today also, indulging herself in this pleasure, when she'd awakened from her doze, Kimie was loath to raise her head from the pillow, although aware that it was nearly three o'clock. Looking around her, she saw the clothes that she'd stripped off herself the night before and her sash lying in a disorderly pile. After the dancer Kimura had left, the automobile importer Yata had come to this four-and-a-half-mat room at the back of the second floor. This morning he had gone, leaving a rain shutter open for her. Dangling from the ceiling, the light bulb still cast the shadow of the flower arrangement against the wall of the ornamental alcove. Carrying the cries of vendors and the languid sounds of song practice, a breeze that flowed along the narrow openings between houses came in at the window, caressing her face where she had flung herself cheek down on the mat. At a moment like this, Kimie wished that Yata or indeed any man were here. She would throw all the desires in her body at him. Forlorn in her fantasies that surged up more and more powerfully, lightly closing her eyes, Kimie embraced herself with all the strength in her arms. Heaving a sigh, she wrestled amorously with her own body. Just then, there was the sound of the opaque paper door softly sliding open. A man stepped into the room and stood in front of the folding screen. It was none other than Kimura Yoshio, whom Kimie had been thinking of so regretfully since last night.

"Well." Just barely raising her face, Kimie did not attempt to get up. Gazing at him from where she lay, she held out her arms, waiting for Kimura to bend down to her. Pulling him close, she murmured: "I was dreaming about you."

A while later, Kimura told Kimie that he had lost a silver filigree pencil the evening before and come back on the off chance that it might be here.

When the two had gotten up and were putting their

chopsticks to a fish in the front parlor, a phonecall came
from the waitress Ruriko. Last night, as requested by
Kimie, she had gone to Honmura-cho and assuming an
agitated demeanor had informed Kiyooka that Kimie had
been taken against her will to the Chiyoda assignation
house in Sanban-cho. Abruptly displeased and not listening to her explanations, Kiyooka had shaken her off
along the way and gone somewhere by himself. Anxious
to let Kimie know, Ruriko had waited for her to come
to the restaurant. But when she'd failed to appear even
for the three o'clock shift, Ruriko had gotten in touch
with Kimie's landlady through the fish dealer's. Surmising the situation from the old woman's answer, she had
then called here.

It was dark by the time Kimie and Kimura completed
their repast. Announcing that he had an opening day
tomorrow at the Maruen Theater and must go for re-
hearsal, Kimura made hasty preparations to leave. Handing Kimie five or six special-price tickets and asking her
to sell them to the waitresses at the cafe, he departed,
without paying either for the meal or the taxicab fare.

Kimie, just as if she'd been amusing herself with a
storyteller or a kind of male geisha, felt a sudden letdown.
The carefully nurtured illusion that all day she had been
living in a dream had already faded away. With the last of
the light, the fact that for the time being at least she had
nothing to do tonight came home to her with an abrupt
loneliness. She could not stay by herself at the assignation
house. Paying Kimura's bill for food and drink, she went
outside. It was the hour when the coming and going of
geishas to their engagements was at its height. It was too
late to go to the cafe, yet too early to go home. Thinking on the spur of the moment that she would go see

Kyoyo at the Paulownia Blossom House, Kimie had no
sooner turned the corner than, coming toward her, holding up the skirts of her banquet kimono, the edges of her
red undergarments aflutter in the evening breeze, in full
geisha regalia, was none other than Kyoyo.

"Kimi-san. Are you on your way to the Ginza?"

"It's already too late. I thought I'd take the night off."

"You've been at the Chiyoda house, haven't you?"

"How did you know?"

"How did I know, nothing. Kimi-chan. You mustn't
go there. Last night I saw Mr. Kiyooka."

"You did?" Kimie's eyes widened in surprise, as well
they might.

"Yes. I saw Mr. Kiyooka during the evening at the
Noda house. He was with three or four people. I was on
my way to an after-engagement, so I just caught a glimpse
of him. At the time, I didn't notice who it was. But I
saw his friends later, and I heard all about their conversation. All the geishas know that you occasionally go to
the Chiyoda. The houses are right next to each other, and
you can see everything from the window. In the banquet
room, they were talking away about you without knowing that it was Mr. Kiyooka. Well, anyway, we can't talk
here. I have business with the old woman, so tomorrow
or the day after I'll come by for a good long chat. But you
really ought to stay away from that place."

"So. It was that sort of thing, was it? Well, I'll wait for
your visit."

Dogs of the neighborhood, samisen carriers, shopboys
delivering cooked food, geishas, and the like were passing by in an endless stream. Quickly ending their chance
encounter, the pair parted and went their separate ways.

EIGHT

SINCE her husband generally got up toward noon, each morning Tsuruko would have her solitary breakfast of milk and toast instead of the usual rice, clean out the cage of the parrot she'd kept the past several years, water the bonsai, do up her hair, get dressed, and wait for her lord and master to arise. This morning, among the mail that the maid brought her with the milk, there was a letter with both the address and name written in Western characters. Casually picking it up, Tsuruko discovered it was for her. The handwriting was familiar. It was from Madame Joule, the French lady from whom she had taken lessons for more than two years before and after her graduation from girls' school.

Madame Joule, wife of the noted Orientalist Alphonse Joule, had accompanied her husband to the East, living in China for upward of ten years and afterward for several years in Japan. At one time she had returned to her own country, but after her husband's death, to console herself for her widowhood she had traveled by herself in America and later returned to Japan, where she'd lived in Tokyo for a couple of years. It was during this period that Tsuruko and two or three of her schoolfriends had studied French and etiquette with her. After Madame Joule's return to Paris, an urgent matter had arisen in connection with the posthumous publication of her husband's work. And so four or five days ago she had once again returned to Japan. She was staying at the Imperial Hotel and wished Tsuruko to come and visit her.

Tsuruko, after waiting until the noon siren for Susumu
to bestir himself, telephoned the hotel and set out.

Madame Joule was a plump, genial, round-faced lady
with narrow eyes and flaccid cheeks, such as one often
sees among foreign women of a certain age. Her modern
Japanese was quite passable, and she could even read a
little of the old Chinese-style compositions. In her ability
to look up words in *An Etymology of the Chinese Language*,
she may well have excelled present-day Japanese students.

It being the luncheon hour, Madame Joule led Tsuruko
to a table in the hotel dining room. In connection with the
compilation of her late husband's work, she told Tsuruko,
her first task was to make up for a lack of photographs of
shrines, temples, and old utensils by buying up a number
of these. Her second task was to locate a suitable Japanese
to accompany her back to France, a person to whom she
could entrust the organization of the numerous volumes
of Oriental paintings and writings that were stored away
at her principal residence. When Tsuruko inquired what
degree of scholarship was necessary, Madame Joule replied that she wasn't particularly looking for a specialist.
If, for instance, the person could distinguish between a
tanka and a *ha-uta*,* that would suffice. Rather than scholarship, she was looking for a person possessed of the taste
and discrimination peculiar to the Japanese and also of a
modicum of French. Such a person would leave nothing
to be desired. Madame Joule continued: "The work will
be completed in about half a year. If you were single and
at liberty, I would certainly ask you. But since that is no
longer the case, I must ask you to recommend somebody
you know."

*A *tanka* is a poem of thirty-one syllables; a *ha-uta* is a short
popular song (tr. note).

Hearing these words, Tsuruko nearly pushed the table back in her excitement. Almost forgetting herself, she leaned across the table and said: "If it's for half a year or a year, I . . . if someone like myself would be of use, no matter what arrangements were necessary, I'd like to go with you."

"Would you be able to?" Madame Joule's eyes widened in surprise and pleasure.

"I've always thought I would like to go to the West just once." Trying not to show the emotion that had instantly welled up in her, Tsuruko lowered her voice.

Until she had received Madame Joule's letter this morning, come to the hotel, and sat down at the lunch table, Tsuruko had never so much as dreamed that a great change like this could occur in her life. There was nothing so difficult to calculate as fate. As she had listened to Madame Joule's conversation, Tsuruko, as if suddenly laid under a spell, found herself longing to go to some distant place. Tsuruko had known for some time that whether what awaited her at her destination was good or bad, it was necessary first to leave her husband's house to find a new life. But until today, she had not had the chance to act on that knowledge. At one point, in deep despair, she had decided that everything was her punishment for the error she'd committed. There was nothing for it but to grow old quickly, to wait for the day when the regret and sadness of half a lifetime would be no more than a tea-time story. Now, however, an extraordinary opportunity had come her way. There was no time to waste thinking about this and that. If, in the past, obstacles had arisen because of her habitual hesitation, Tsuruko felt that now the energy to expel the latter with all her strength, to do what was in her mind, had come to her.

After lunch, as she and the old lady sat on a sofa in the corridor and sipped coffee, their friendly conversation went on for another hour or so. Leaving the hotel, blithely unconcerned about the steamy noonday heat that had suddenly followed a clearing in the rainy-season cloud cover, Tsuruko caught a cab at the Hibiya intersection and went out to Setagaya to pay her husband's old father a visit. When she told him about the proposed trip to the West, Akira replied that during his teaching days at the university he had met Professor Joule two or three times. "When you get there, if there's anything in the books you don't understand, feel free to write me and ask." More and more overjoyed at the prospect of leaving home, Tsuruko hurried back while the long summer evening was still bright with sunlight to get her husband's permission. But Kiyooka had already gone out. Toward midnight the usual message came that since it was late she was not to wait up for him. Tsuruko had no choice but to go to bed. The next morning, since her husband was not there for her to wait for him to get up, she left a note saying that she'd been requested to do something by Madame Joule, and once more set out for the hotel. Madame Joule intended the following day to go to Kyoto, and also to visit Nara. Sojourning two or three days in Nagasaki, she planned to return to Kobe and wait for the first available steamer. Asking Tsuruko to make ready for that day, and to come to the hotel in Kobe, she wrote out a detailed schedule of her movements. To expedite the matter of Tsuruko's passport, Madame Joule would have the French embassy deal directly with the authorities concerned.

It wasn't until late the following evening, when all the world was asleep, that Tsuruko met with her husband for the first time and told him her plans for a trip abroad.

Susumu, although so surprised that he instantly sobered up from the sake he'd been drinking somewhere, spoke with deliberate nonchalance. "Is that so? It's all right with me. You may go."

"The agreement is for half a year, but if all goes well, I'm thinking I'd like to return earlier."

"There's no particular need to hurry back. It'd be too much trouble to go again, so take your time, study and sightsee and things like that."

The conversation of the two went no further than this. Susumu, although surmising the thoughts that lay behind this trip of Tsuruko's, decided that it was already too late at this point to detain her. If he were to put on a regretful air, it would be mortifying to have her think: "Well, in that case he might have been a little kinder to me in the past." If, on the other hand, he assumed an indifferent attitude that would make her think that he'd been waiting for her to go away, he would feel as if his deepest desire had been seen through. The best thing was to adopt an ambiguous attitude that was not quite either of the two. This way of approaching the matter was the same, as far as that went, for Tsuruko herself. If she were to put on an air of sorrowful parting, it would be a nuisance to be forcibly detained. On the other hand, if she were to act overly cool, it would of course be undesirable to be thought a shallow, unfeeling woman. Husband and wife, covertly observing each other, doing their best not to touch on the real state of affairs, aimed at concluding this scene peaceably and in good form.

About a week later, Tsuruko boarded the evening express train for Kobe. Although there had been talk among Susumu's friends of a farewell banquet, Tsuruko, saying that she wanted to avoid having her name appear in the newspapers and seen by her family, resolutely rejected the idea. The party that saw her off at Tokyo Station numbered only her husband, Susumu, and his disciple Muraoka, the student-houseboy Noguchi, and two or three of her schoolfriends, each of whom was now respectably married. Her elder brother, although sanctioning the trip to the extent of secretly providing travel expenses, did not come to see her off for fear of what people would say. The old man in Setagaya, also, pleading his advanced years, did not come to the station.

When the train had pulled out, two of the men, Susumu in the fore, and the ladies naturally fell out into separate groups as they made their way out of the station. Only Muraoka, hat in hand, stood gazing after the train even when it had disappeared. Looking around, Susumu barked: "Hey, Muraoka, what are you standing there staring at?"

"It was such a lonely departure." Looking around him at the already deserted platform, only now did Muraoka begin walking.

"Thus ends Book One of *The Life Story of Tsuruko.*" With this comment, Kiyooka tossed his half-smoked cigarette onto the tracks.

"Even so, she's coming back in six months."

"Oh, she'll come back all right. But it probably won't be to my house."

"Sensei, I had that feeling myself. Today was a sort of sign."

"Hey, Muraoka, why didn't you become her youthful paramour? I could see it all. She was looking for a sentimental, comparatively pure young man like yourself."

Muraoka, a youth still shy of his thirtieth birthday, blushed crimson. "Sensei, don't make that kind of joke. It's not true. That kind of thing."

"Ha ha ha. It won't be too late even after she gets back."

For the first time, Kiyooka smiled as if he were genuinely amused.

When they got to the ticket gate, the three were suddenly engulfed in a crowd of people coming and going. Breaking off their conversation, they emerged from the station. The evening wind, after rain, was blowing lonely and desolate, chill against the skin.

"Hey, Noguchi, it's still early, so you can go and see a movie. Here's a complimentary ticket." Sending the houseboy on his way, Susumu aimlessly strolled along with Muraoka among the crowds of pedestrians beneath the Maru Building. As if he'd suddenly remembered, Muraoka said: "Sensei, what about the Don Juan? Is it all over?"

"Hm. I've been doing a little thinking about that."

"What sort of thinking?"

"Well, I still don't have anything particular in mind. I don't intend to bother you about it, though, so rest easy. Your trouble is, you're too good a person."

"Is that so? I wonder."

"Sometimes you say things that sound just like some old man in the country."

"Even so, I don't think you should hold a grudge against Kimie-san the way you do."

"That's because you're only an onlooker. It's not that I dislike her that much. She just annoys me. It's nothing as serious as revenge or retaliation. I just want to make things a little hard for her. If I told you what I had in mind, you'd be sure to say that it was cruel or departed from the path of virtue or something."

"What exactly do you have in mind?"

"It's not that I don't trust you, but I can't talk about it right now."

"Are you going to report her to the police?"

"Don't be a fool. If I did something like that, Kimie would think nothing of it. They'd hold her for two or three days, and she'd come out free as a bird. Even if she isn't a waitress, there are plenty of things she can do. . . . I want to do something to her so she won't be able to do anything. I want to set up some situation in which I won't have to lay a hand on her—others will do it for me. Ha ha ha. It's a fantasy of mine. No, as a matter of fact, I've been thinking a lot lately about writing a short story about this kind of psychological state in a man. I believe it's the theme of one of Balzac's stories. A husband seals up the closet in which his wife's lover is hiding into a wall. Then he sits and drinks wine in front of it with the unfaithful wife. In my fantasy . . . in the story I'm thinking of writing, I'd like to strip the woman stark naked and throw her out of a taxicab on some thoroughfare like the Ginza. It would be amusing also to tie her up to a tree in Hibiya Park. In the old days, they used to expose adulterous couples to public view at the approach to Nihonbashi Bridge. That sort of thing. What do you think? Perhaps the contemporary reader wouldn't accept such a story."

Muraoka could not tell whether Susumu was actually talking about the plot for a story, teasing him for the fun of it, or, pretending it was for a story, speaking obliquely of his plans for revenge on Kimie. But he was vaguely aware of something ominous, as if all his hairs were about to rise and stand on end. Forcing himself, he said: "It sounds interesting. Readers are getting tired of sugary love scenes."

"It might be amusing also to set fire to the place where she was staying with her lover. Then, when she ran outside in her rumpled nightgown, grab her under cover of the confusion, take her off somewhere, and do whatever one felt like doing to her."

"Indeed."

"There's something else I have in mind . . ."

"Sensei, please stop. Somehow it gives me a bad feeling. Please stop."

"It looks as if we're going to have a storm tonight."

The sky had clouded over blackly and looked as if it would send the rain down any minute. In the interstices of the clouds, tattered by the violent wind, stars were appearing and disappearing. From the sidewalk trees, thrashing in the wind, the delicate new leaves, so freshly green, went flying helter-skelter to the pavement. Amid the wind and the gathering darkness, the streets of this Marunouchi district, which at night tended to empty of passers-by, seemed all the lonelier. One had the feeling that muggers might spring out from the narrow streets between the towering buildings.

"There's a story about an actress from the Imperial Theater who was hit and dragged by a car on her way home. She lost a leg. The person who did it was never caught."

"Is that so? That kind of thing has happened, has it?"

"Then there was the geisha who had her eyes rubbed with germs while she was asleep and went blind. A woman like Kimie is sure to meet a similar fate. . . ."

Suddenly there was a gasp from Susumu. Startled, Muraoka stepped closer to him. A gust of wind from the side had snatched Susumu's expensive panama off his head.

Without noticing it, they'd come almost as far as the *Nichi-Nichi* newspaper building. Somewhat fatigued, they stopped to rest at a small cafe in the neighborhood. After

Susumu had had a whiskey and Muraoka a beer, they followed their feet toward the Ginza. When Muraoka tried to separate and go his own way, he was prevented by Kiyooka. Tonight, the latter said, he meant to study conditions in back-street cafes where his face wasn't known. In rapid succession, they visited five or six cafes. Having four or five whiskies in each cafe, even the heavy drinker Kiyooka was rather unsteady on his legs tonight. He was about to enter another cafe along the way when Muraoka plucked at his sleeve.

"Sensei, let's stop this. Let's go to some place that's not a cafe. I'm tired out."

"What the hell time is it?"

"It's already twelve o'clock."

"It's already that late?"

"That's why I've had enough of these cafes."

Thinking that at any rate it was risky for Kiyooka to wander around this area in a drunken state, and that at least they would be safe in an assignation house, Muraoka went on: "Sensei, let's have a quiet drink someplace where we can relax."

"Hm. You're quite talkative tonight, aren't you? All right, take me to some place you like."

"Let's catch a taxi then, sensei."

Immediately tugging at the sleeve of Kiyooka's haori, Muraoka began to head for the recently opened thoroughfare of West Ginza, which ran toward Chichibashi Bridge.

"Wait. Wait."

Kiyooka had begun to piss against the wall of a pitch-dark building. Muraoka, standing a short ways off at the corner, idly watched as three women, evidently waitresses, happened to pass by. Abruptly, he realized that one of them was Kimie of the Don Juan. Kimie, also, see-

113

ing Muraoka, seemed to utter a cry—*ara* or *oya*—but the
violent wind, which even now hadn't left off, bore her
voice away unheard. Muraoka, instantly recalling what
Kiyooka had said as they'd strolled through Marunouchi
a while back, feeling some unidentifiable fear, desperately signaled her with his head and hands to quickly go
away. If Kiyooka, who unusually for him was dead drunk
tonight, were suddenly to catch sight of Kimie on this
deserted back street, there was no telling what he might
do. If he caused a ruckus that got into the newspapers, it
would be a disaster.

Kimie, whether she had guessed Muraoka's meaning
or not it was impossible to tell, passed by without further ado. As, with her companions, she was about to
enter a noodle shop across the way, Kiyooka, who'd just
then completed a very long piss, swaying slightly, gazed
after them.

"Who are those waitresses over there? I'm going to
treat them."

In consternation, Muraoka clung to his sleeve. "Please
don't. There seems to be a strange man following them."

"What the hell do I care? I'm going to treat them."

"Sensei, please don't." Holding him back with all the
strength in his arms, Muraoka hailed a passing one-yen
taxi. Although in the confusion he hadn't been aware of
it, a misty rain had begun to mingle with the wind. After
getting in the cab, he noticed that the outsides of the
windowpanes were wet.

The three women, who after leaving the noodle shop
caught a cab, were Ruriko, Haruyo, and Kimie. Ruriko
got off first, in Akasaka-Hitotsugi. Next, Haruyo got
off in Yotsuya-Samon. The driver, who'd been given the

destination beforehand, turning off the trolley avenue in Shiomachi, started down the Tsu no Kami Slope. At dead of night, with a drizzling rain, the streets were completely deserted. Kimie, intoxicated, began to grow sleepy as soon as she was by herself. Do what she would, she could not keep her eyes open. All of a sudden, she heard a man's voice say: "Kimiko." Surprised, Kimie realized that the voice calling out what he thought was her name was that of the driver, whom she'd never seen before. While thinking him a terrible oaf, Kimie decided that he must have been listening to their conversation and was trying to be funny. Paying him no mind, she said: "Ah, here we are in Honmura-cho."

Slowing the taxi to a crawl, the driver went on: "Right from the start, I thought it was you, Kimiko. You haven't forgotten me, have you? I met you two or three times at the Kato house in Suwamachi." Taking off his cap, he turned around and showed her his face.

The Kato house in Suwamachi had been where Kyoyo had worked before moving on to Fujimi-cho. Now that the driver had said so, Kimie thought that he must indeed have been a customer of hers on several occasions. Having long since forgotten his face, though, she could not remember him at all. It was not that Kimie hadn't given some thought to the appropriate attitude to adopt if she should encounter a client from that time among the customers at the cafe. But, Tokyo being the huge city it was, although Kimie had been employed at one cafe or another for nearly half a year now, from her first day on the Ginza down to today she hadn't met a single client from that other time. As the days and months had gone by, she'd naturally relaxed her vigilance, only to be abruptly accosted tonight by a taxicab driver. Although flabbergasted, as she well might be, Kimie decided the best thing was to brazen it out with a know-nothing face.

"You must have the wrong person. I don't know what you're talking about."

"It's not strange you've forgotten me, Kimiko. Because I've fallen so low in the world I'm driving a one-yen taxi. But you haven't risen so high yourself. After all, you're just a waitress. Even a waitress is no different from a high-class lady of the night, eh?"

"Let me out, please. Right here's fine."

"But it's raining. Let me drive you back to your place."

"It's all right. I don't want to inconvenience you."

"Kimiko-san, back then, you charged ten yen."

"I said, let me out. Why aren't you stopping? Do you think I'd be out late at night if I were afraid of men? You fool."

At Kimie's show of fearlessness, the driver, perhaps because he thought that even if he tried force it wouldn't work, obediently brought the car to a stop. Just then, a gust of wind blew the rain against the window. As if to say "serves you right for not having brought an umbrella," the driver reached back and opened the door from inside.

"If here's all right for you. Get out, please."

"I'm leaving one yen here." Tossing a couple of silver fifty-sen coins onto the seat, Kimie started to get out. Timing the exact moment her foot touched the ground, the driver suddenly stepped on the gas. The car shot forward. Kimie, screaming, went flying head over heels out into the rain.

"Look at you now, you whore." The driver's jeering voice was drowned out by the sound of the rain. The car immediately sped off into the night.

Coming to herself, Kimie sat up in the mud and looked around her. Although she'd thought that this place was the pitch-dark road that ran from the base of the Tsu no Kami Slope to the police substation in Sakamachi, she now saw that it was a neighborhood of walled residential compounds. She had no idea where she was. There were no cars passing by, and of course no passers-by. Dragging herself along, she came to a pair of stone gateway posts surmounted by lamps. Under the provisional shelter of the foliage of an oak that reached its branches over the wall, Kimie began to do up her hair, disheveled from the rain and clogged with mud. Stroking her forehead, she looked at her palm. It was sticky with blood. The instant she knew there was blood on her face, Kimie's pulse began to pound. The heart to care about her hair and clothes went out of her. Just barely controlling an impulse to cry out for help, she set out at a run through the rain in search of a doctor's office or a pharmacy.

NINE

THE doctor, whose office was on Yakuoji-maemachi Avenue at the top of Ichigaya-Kappa Slope, not only gave Kimie emergency aid but called a cab for her. The rainy night was beginning to lighten toward dawn by the time she returned to her rented room in Honmura-cho. The cuts and scratches on her face, hands, and legs were not that serious. However, thanks to her not having taken off her soaking-wet clothes all night, from daybreak on her temperature gradually rose, climbing past forty degrees centigrade. Even by the following evening, it showed no signs of going down. Saying that there was a risk of typhus or pneumonia, the doctor gave instructions to the old woman. Luckily, however, things did not develop that far. By the third day, talk of hospitalization was dropped, and by the end of the week Kimie was allowed to sit up in bed.

Thinking not only that it would be a nuisance to have a stream of bedside callers if people found out about her mishap, but that rumors of rape might even arise, Kimie decided to merely inform the cafe that she was laid up with a cold. On the afternoon of the eighth day, Haruyo came around to see her for the first time. By then, the bandage on her forehead had been removed, and Kimie could explain away the scars with a story about having tripped and fallen in the alley that night. The next day, Ruriko came by, but she also went away thinking only that Kimie had caught a heavy cold. Kimie's temperature slowly sank to normal, and her appetite came back. As yet, though, the bruises around her hips and on her arms and legs hadn't healed. When she went down or came up the ladder-stairs, she sometimes felt pain. The old woman having told her about a bathhouse with medicated waters in Ichigaya-mitsuke, Kimie went that evening. The next day, by forcing herself a little, she would do her coiffure, she decided.

When Kimie got back from the bathhouse, a letter had arrived for her. Although there was no return address, as she read it became clear that the letter was from Kiyooka's disciple, Muraoka.

"I have written this letter after debating with myself whether in fact I should write such a letter. That is because if my mentor Kiyooka-san were to find out about it, it would likely mean the end of our relationship. However, believing that you feel sufficient friendship toward me to keep the matter a secret, I have written this letter. I don't know whether you are aware of this, but late last month Kiyooka-san's wife abruptly left Japan in the company of a certain foreign lady. Kiyooka-san pretends that this parting has occasioned no great emotion in him, but his behavior gives the pretense away. In the ten days or so since his wife's departure, what with drinking and dissipation the sensei's life has suddenly gone to seed. It is my belief that it is only your love, Kimie-san, that has the power to console the sensei in his present and future life. Of course, nowadays, the sensei avoids the very mention of your name in front of us. . . . But from that very avoidance, from that alone, I deduce that the sensei is still unable to efface the thought of you from his inmost heart. It occurs to me that the sensei is attempting to fix the blame on you alone for his having lost his wife. I shall have to tell you everything that has happened since last year. My making bold to inform you of the plots of revenge that have been continually hatching at the bottom of the sensei's heart ever since last year is not to estrange you and the sensei from each other. Rather, it is a spirit of duty, a sincere desire that you should know just how much the sensei loves you, even to the point of imagining bloodthirsty things against you. In two or three days, the sensei will be traveling from Sendai to the Aomori district, in order to deliver a lecture at a literary conference sponsored by the Maruen Publishing Company. The sensei has expressed his intention of escaping the heat this summer at some hot-springs inn in the Northeast. I myself have not set foot in my own part of the country in a long time, so after seeing the sensei off I intend to take advantage of his absence to leave Tokyo for a while. Wanting to see you once before then, I went to the Don Juan yesterday. I was informed that you were sick in bed. I am forced to feel grateful that your illness has prevented you from going out these past several days. I will say no more than that. If I say that I hesitate to state the reason, I believe you will instantly guess all. So then, I will be in the country until that time of year when the autumn wind shakes the stems of the tall-grown dahlias. I look forward to meeting you on the Ginza in the cool of the evening when the crowds are lively once more.

July 4th."

Observing the letter's date, Kimie felt as if she'd realized only now that it was July. She also felt as if the incident of barely ten days ago had taken place a month or two months in the past. That was how long she felt she had been in bed. Simply not having gone to the cafe, where she'd been working every day for more than a year now, made her feel as if her life had completely changed. The rains were suddenly over. The sky was absolutely clear. During the day, a cool breeze blew continuously, but ceased at nightfall. The night turned hot and steamy. Even when she sat still, greasy sweat poured off Kimie. In contrast to the rainy season quietude of until just yesterday, the narrow back alley jammed with little houses suddenly came alive with people's voices and the sound of sewing machines doing piecework. On the streets outside the alley, radios had started up amid a variety of other, unidentifiable noises. Called downstairs by the old woman, Kimie ate supper. Afterward, her freshly washed hair not yet done up into a coiffure, with only a perfunctory dusting of face powder, she sallied out into the world beyond the alley. Not only was it bothersome to be talked at every night by the old woman, but with the sudden advent of midsummer she wanted to be out of the house, out walking somewhere, it didn't matter where. When, just before leaving, she'd taken out her purse from a drawer of the mirror-stand, Muraoka's letter had caught her eye. Just so, she'd slipped it together with the purse between her obi and kimono. What with the gathering dusk and being called downstairs to supper, she had only skimmed the second half of the letter by the dim light from the window. Kimie meant to stroll along the Moat and find a quiet place at the edge of the embankment where she could read the letter again under a bright park lamp. But traffic was heavy along the Moat, and she still hadn't found a suitable place by the time she had come as far as the New Approach. Ahead, the lights of the boat rental pier at the Ushigome Approach were visible. Two or three girls, apparently students, were sitting on a fence that lined the Approach, enjoying the evening cool. Taking advantage of the fact that her yukata with its pattern of interwoven ivy leaves was not overly conspicuous, Kimie loitered at a slight distance. Letting the wind blow against her loosely bound hair, she opened the letter by the light of a park lamp. The letter's style seemed to Kimie as affected as that of a schoolboy's love letter, as circumlocutory as something one might read in a translated novel, and even gave her a weird feeling somehow. But she found it difficult to make out which were the facts and which rhetorical flourishes. If one were to briefly summarize the letter's contents, it seemed that since Kiyooka had in effect made Kimie his second wife, his first wife had run out on him and so she, Kimie, would have to do something. If she went on pretending to know nothing, there was no telling what desperate revenge Kiyooka might attempt to wreak on her. Muraoka seemed to be cautioning Kimie to forestall such an event as best she could. As she thought it over, Kimie grew more and more angry at a man who could write such senseless, unreasonable things.

After a while, it occurred to Kimie that this letter was no spontaneous outpouring of Muraoka's heart but something that he'd been put up to by Kiyooka. Recalling Muraoka's behavior that night when she had unexpectedly encountered them on the West Ginza as she'd been about to enter a noodle shop with her friends, Kimie thought it quite possible that her having been thrown out of the cab later on that night was Kiyooka's handiwork. Along with a sense of fear like a sudden cold gust against the nape of her neck, Kimie felt defiance surge up in her. Kiyooka might be Kiyooka, but Kimie was Kimie. She was not about to knuckle under to him. He could do anything he liked, she didn't care.

Since she could not stand forever in the same place,

Kimie moved on, thinking and thinking as she passed the Approach. By the edge of the embankment in Yonban-cho where there is a public garden, she found a bench under a park lamp and sat down. Probably because it was a Sunday, there were none of the usual students about, teasing young women on their way home from night school. At the foot of the embankment, directly beneath her, and along the avenue across the waters of the Moat, there was a continual coming and going of trolleys. In the intervals of their passing, from the surface of the dark water the voices of young women floated up, mingling with the quiet sound of oars. Every summer, when the Moat became lively with rented boats, Kimie always thought back to the time when she lived together with Kyoko in the house in Koishikawa bought by the latter's patron. Any number of times, rowing out to the middle of the Moat where the lights from shore did not reach, they had deliberately bumped into boats with only men in them, using that as their cue for seduction. Since that time, down to this day, a period of three or four years, various riotous scenes of Kimie's lewd and self-indulgent life, about which she could tell no one, had unfolded against the backdrop of this moatside view from Iidabashi to the Ichigaya Approach. At the thought, the feeling came to Kimie that somehow or other the curtain raiser of this latest incident was naturally drawing to an end. . . .

Aroused from her revery by a tiger moth that grazed her cheek like a flung pebble, Kimie gazed once more at the view that stretched from Ushigome to Koishikawa. Suddenly, somehow, it all became dear to her. Feeling that she would like to fix the scene in her heart, so that even if she never saw it again she would have no regrets, so that it would not fade out of her memory for a long, long

time, Kimie stood up from the bench and went toward
the wire fence. Just then, like a quivering shadow, a man
approached out of the darkness under the trees. Kimie
very nearly bumped into him. As they each veered out of
the other's way, their eyes met.

"Ya–a. Kimiko–san."

"Uncle, what are you doing around here?" In their
surprise, the two stood where they were. "Uncle" was
the patron who had bought out the contract of Kyoko,
the geisha from Ushigome, and installed her in a house
in Gyutenshin. When Kimie had run away from home
and was staying at Kyoko's house, the geishas who continually came there for visits always referred to him as
"uncle." Imitating them, Kimie had also called him that.
His name was Kawashima Kinnosuke. Formerly he had
been in charge of the stock department of a certain company. When it was discovered that he'd misappropriated
funds, however, he'd been sent to prison. In the old days,
he had been wont to dress as stylishly as a professional
entertainer, going about in Yuki pongee silk and the like.
Now, however, not even wearing a hat, he was garbed in
a laundry-faded towel-cloth yukata, cinched at the waist
with an undress obi, his feet shod in cheap wooden clogs.
Something about him suggested that he'd only recently
emerged from prison.

Drawing together his towel-cloth kimono at the neck
as if he were cold, Kawashima said: "I'm not the person
I was. The past is the past, the present is the present."
Although forcing a smile to his lips, the man seemed unaccountably agitated, constantly on the lookout from the
corners of his eyes. Back then, Kawashima had already
been forty-five or -six years old, but his white hairs hadn't
been particularly noticeable. Seen from behind, accom-

panied by his young concubine, his medium-build figure had seemed that of an exceptionally well-turned-out man in the prime of life. Now, however, his strangely yellowed face was gouged with deep wrinkles, and his bushy hair, which looked as if he'd been showered with dust and ashes, was all white and unkempt. His eyes, which before had been lively and sparkling, now glittered eerily in their deep-sunken sockets as if staring out at something.

"Back then, you did a lot of things for me." At a loss for a greeting, Kimie thanked Kawashima as if only now remembering to.

"Still hanging around this area, are you?"

"I'm in Honmura-cho. In Ichigaya."

"So. Well then, we'll probably meet again somewhere."

With this, the two had started to move past each other when it occurred to Kimie that she would like to at least know where he lived. Walking along two or three steps with him, she inquired subtly: "Uncle, have you seen Kyoko? Since then, I haven't seen her again."

"Oh? I heard something about her being in Fujimi-cho. But if I went the way I am now, she wouldn't let me get near her. So it's better not to go."

"No, it's not like that at all. Do go and see her."

"What have you been doing since that time, Kimiko-san? I suppose you've found some man you like and are living together."

"No, Uncle. It's the same as before. I ended up becoming a waitress. Although I've been sick in bed this last week or so."

"Is that so? A waitress, eh?"

The two walked along talking. As well as young couples sitting together on the benches under the trees, there were a few passers-by, who also seemed to be student types. Apparently somewhat reassured, Kawashima sat down of his own accord on a nearby bench.

"There are a lot of things I'd like to ask you about. Seeing your face brings back the past. Even though I thought I'd forgotten about the past . . ."

"Uncle, when I think of it, that time when I was staying at your place in Suwamachi was the most fun. Even before, by myself, I was thinking of it and got lost in memories. Tonight has really been a strange night. Just as I was thinking about the old days and staring off in a daze toward Koishikawa, then I met you, Uncle. It really is strange."

"That's so. You can see Koishikawa quite clearly from here." His attention caught by the view beyond the Moat, Kawashima also gazed across the water. "That brightly lit place over there is the Kagura Slope. That means the Ando Slope is over there. And that place with all the trees is Gyutenshin. Yes, I carried on just as I pleased in those days. If there is just one time in one's life when one has enjoyed oneself, it's worth having been born. And when the time comes to give it up, you've got to resign yourself."

"That's true. That's why I've been thinking of going back to the country. Even as a waitress, although I don't particularly care one way or another, because of some trivial incident I've been badly thought of and had grudges held against me. It's unpleasant, and when I think of what might happen to me, I somehow feel frightened. . . . Uncle, about ten days ago, I was thrown out of a taxicab and was injured. I still have the scars. See? And there's one on my arm." Kimie rolled up the sleeve of her yukata and showed Kawashima.

"You poor girl. You've had a rough time of it. Was it a lover's grudge?"

"Uncle, men are far more unforgiving than women. Recently, I've thought that for the first time."

"When you think about it, men are no different from women."

"So you've thought the same thing, Uncle. From those days when you were having a good time . . ."

Suddenly, from the foot of the embankment, the sound of a train going by arose with a cloud of coal smoke, drowning out Kawashima's reply and obscuring the farther view. Covering her face with her sleeve, Kimie stood up. Kawashima also got to his feet.

"Well, let's move on. If it's not too much trouble, I'd like to have your address at least."

"Ichigaya, Honmura-cho, number 90. It's near Kamesaki. I'm always in till noon or one o'clock. Where are you living now, Uncle?"

"Me? Well, I . . . If I find a place, I'll let you know."

There was only one path through the park. Before they knew it, Kimie and Kawashima had come out at the New Approach and onto the trolley avenue alongside the Moat. Since it was only a one-stop ride to Ichigaya, Kimie thought she would walk back after seeing Kawashima off on the trolley. As she stood waiting with him, however, Kawashima—in which direction was he going?—let two or three trolleys pass with no attempt to board them. Not resuming their conversation just yet, again walking side by side without really seeming to, step by step, the two neared the Ichigaya Approach.

"Uncle, it's right over there, so come in for a moment." If she went back to the country, there was no telling when she would see him again. Kimie somehow had a lonely feeling. She also felt that as a return for all his past favors, she would like if she could to cheer him up with stories about the old days.

"It's no trouble for you?"

"Of course it isn't. Come along."

"You have a rented room, I suppose."

"Yes. I have the whole second floor to myself. There's nobody but the old woman downstairs. You don't have to be afraid of anybody."

"In that case, I'll impose on your hospitality a moment."

"Yes, come up. Whenever it's a man, even if it's just a social call, the old woman is terribly tactful and leaves the house. She's a little *too* alert. It makes me feel bad."

When they turned off the avenue along the Moat into the alley, as luck would have it the young man from the sake shop was cooling himself on the sidewalk outside. Kimie ordered three beers and some tinned crab from him. Sliding open the door of the entryway, she called out: "Auntie, I'm back," and ushered Kawashima upstairs. During her absence, the old woman had evidently done some cleaning up. A scrap of Yuzen silk had been hung over the mirror of the dressing-stand, and in the six-mat room bedding had already been laid out. Kawashima, standing in the doorway, looked around the room as if surprised. Only his glittering eyes showed anything, however, so that Kimie guessed nothing. "The old woman thinks I'm still sick. I'll just put this away." Sliding open the door of the wardrobe, Kimie started to put the pillow away.

As if he'd just then returned to himself, Kawashima hurriedly said: "Kimiko-san. Please don't trouble yourself. If I'm treated like a guest, I won't know how to act."

"Well then, I'll leave the bedding as it is. When I was living at O-Kyo-san's place, I was always being told that I never so much as folded up a single kimono. My messi-

128

ness dates from that time, so you know all about it."
Turning over a muslin-covered cushion from in front of
the mirror-stand, Kimie offered it to Kawashima.

The old woman, bringing the beer and the tinned
crab along with some pickles, silently placed them on the
board floor at the head of the ladder-stairs and withdrew.
Hearing her, Kimie got to her feet. Bringing everything
back into the room, she said: "Uncle, if it's fish you want,
I'll treat you to anything you like. The house in front
is a fish store. If I call out the window, they'll deliver
anything."

Kawashima, draining at a single draft the glass of beer
that Kimie had poured out for him, not saying a word,
seemed to be keeping an eye on that part of the neighborhood that could be seen from the window. Kimie,
wondering if this was how fearful of the world a person became once he'd been in prison, felt more and more
sorry for Kawashima as she observed him.

"Perhaps it's because I just got out of bed today, but
despite this heat the breeze feels chilly." Although in fact
she felt unbearably hot, Kimie slid the paper window
halfway shut.

His eyes instantly reddening around the edges with his
second glass of beer, Kawashima said: "Whatever anyone says, the world is women and drink. I've thought of
making another effort and getting back on my feet, but
my health isn't up to it. There's nothing I can do. But
you still have your life before you, Kimiko. You will experience the true savor of life. You were saying that you
might go back to the country, but could you stand it for
half a month? Even I, broken-down as I am, when I see
a red quilt and drink a glass of sake, it all comes back
to me."

"Uncle, you've become quite respectable."

Kimie, although wanting to ask what sort of life Kawa-shima had led since leaving prison, could not ask him straight out and so adopted a roundabout manner of speech. Kawashima seemed to be in a considerably better mood. His voice taking on a tinge of animation, he said: "You can't dance in a sleeveless robe, as they say. So it's for the best. Since I've returned to this vile world, I've lived like a beggar. I've gone without food, let alone drink. If my son were alive, he would have helped me out. But he died of pneumonia while I was in prison. His wife and daughter have been sent back to the country. I can't even sell the girl to be a geisha for another four or five years. It's not that if I asked, people whom I've helped in the past wouldn't do something for me, but sooner than walk around exposing my disgrace I'd rather kill myself, Kimiko-san. Even if I leave this world, this old man has not forgotten the past. He thanks you."

"Oh, Uncle. Talking that way . . . It's you who have helped me, in more ways than I can count. When one comes right down to it, isn't it thanks to you that I've been able to make my own way? You got me that office job at first . . . and then I slowly learned my way around . . . and the things I learned about assignation houses all over Tokyo, and the other things . . . it's all thanks to you, Uncle."

"Ha-ha. Is tonight's beer a thank-you for all the bad things I've taught you? If so, this old man is pleased to accept your hospitality. Even a professional like Kyoko was surprised by you back then. By now, you must really be something."

"Oh, not all that much. I used to go around a great deal with men from the office. I wonder what's become

130

of them all. I've never seen any of them again, not even at the cafe."

"Is that so? That's because they've all gotten older. And that company has gone under. Probably I'm not the only one who's been in straits."

"You, Uncle? You're not all that old yet. I know men of sixty who are all too energetic." About to mention the old gentleman Matsuzaki as an example of what she meant, Kimie checked herself.

"Pleasure, too, when it becomes a habit, is difficult to give up."

"Even for you, Uncle—the past is the past, and so the habit comes right back."

Kimie hadn't had anything to drink for the past ten days or so. As they were talking, the three bottles of beer were quickly emptied.

"Your business has made a very naughty girl of you. Isn't that some whiskey over there?"

"Oh, what with being sick and everything, I'd forgotten all about it." Taking the square bottle of whiskey down from the shelf, Kimie poured some into a teacup. "I don't have any glasses, so please put up with this."

"I've already had too much."

"Well, you'll have some more beer then, or sake?"

"No, nothing more. Drinking again after so long, I'm getting tipsy. It'd be awful if I couldn't go back."

"If you can't go back, you can rest over there. I don't mind." Saying this, Kimie drained at a single gulp the half teacupful of whiskey.

"You waitresses really are splendid drinkers."

"It's better than sake. You don't have a headache afterward." To moisten her burning throat, Kimie drank off a glass of the remaining beer. Giving a deep sigh, she irritatedly combed back with her fingers her freshly washed hair that had begun to tumble across her face. Thinking how much she had developed in just two years, Kawashima could not take his eyes off Kimie. Back then, although there had been what one might call a certain loose quality, something of the innocent maiden had lingered about her shoulders and hips. Now, however, from her cheeks to her chin the profile of her long, narrow face was supremely elegant. The line of her neck and shoulders suggested a more lissome slenderness than before. In her opened yukata, from her bosom to her thighs as she knelt, her flesh was of an inexhaustible fullness. Everything about her, not just particular parts of her body, breathed out a lovely, alluring charm not to be seen in a respectable woman. Such charm, no doubt, was the same in kind as the difference in the everyday demeanor of a tea–ceremony master from that of an ordinary person, or the physical alertness of a swordsman even at his most relaxed. Even though the woman was not being particularly seductive, Kawashima's feelings were aroused despite himself, drawn in by her.

"Uncle, I've gotten a little drunk myself." Breaking her formal seated posture, Kimie eased her legs out to one side and leaned on her elbow against the windowsill. Propping her cheek on her palm, she turned her face in toward the room to let the breeze blow against her hair. Already quite drunk, Kawashima as he watched her from where he sat was fleetingly reminded of Kimie lying in bed, her hair tumbling disheveled from the pillow onto the mat.

Half-closing her eyes, Kimie hummed a line from a popular song. "Samurai Japan . . ." Listening intently, Kawashima seemed to suddenly make up his mind.

Serving himself, he drank off a glass of whiskey at a single draft.

Somehow with a vague sense that she was dreaming, Kimie awoke to find herself—was it because of the heat?—lying on top of the bedding in nothing but her singlet. The whiskey bottle and the beer bottles stood scattered about just as they had been. But the second floor was empty. From the neighbor's in back, a clock was chiming, either eleven or twelve o'clock. Suddenly, Kimie noticed by her pillow a sheet of letter paper folded double. It seemed to be her own stationery, taken from a drawer of the mirror-stand. Opening it as she lay on her side, Kimie saw that it was from Kawashima.

"There's no time to say anything. Last night, when I happened to meet you, I was walking around looking for a place to kill myself. Thanks to you, I was able once more to experience the pleasure of the past, which I had completely despaired of. Now there is nothing in this world that I will regret leaving. By the time you meet with Kyoko and are talking about this, I will most likely no longer be in this world. I am profoundly grateful to you for your kindness. To tell you the truth, in that moment I wanted to take you with me, all unknowing as you were, to that other world. I was shocked at myself. What a terrible thing a man's will is, I thought. So then, farewell. As thanks for your kindness in this world, I will watch over you from that other world. I pray for your future happiness.

Kawashima Kinnosuke"

"Auntie! Auntie!" Leaping up from the bedding, Kimie went on desperately calling out for the old woman.

Flowers in the Shade

ONE

Outside the glass window of the second-floor room rented by this couple was the laundry-drying platform of the house. The day was drawing on toward noon. From nowhere in particular, there was a smell of broiling sardines. Kimono skirts hoisted, the woman who lived in the front part of this floor was busily hanging things out to dry. Her shadow moved about on the frosted outside of the window.

"Ju-chan, today is the last day of the month. Won't you go to the post office for me later on?"

The woman, who had looked around at a man lying in bed reading the newspaper, seemed to be well past thirty. Without even an undersash, her laundry-worn yukata open in front, sitting with one knee raised at the mirror-stand, she was doing up her sleep-disheveled hair into a bun.

"Yes, I'll go. Are there any live coals? These past two or three days, it's gotten much colder." The man still showed no signs of getting up.

"It's that time of year again. Only a month from New Year's." Holding her hair with one hand, with the other the woman drew toward herself the round porcelain brazier. An aluminum teapot was suspended over it.

"Hm. Time certainly goes by quickly. Next year is unlucky for me too."

"That's so. . . . I feel very melancholy about it. A man is in his prime after forty, so he's all right, but a woman is already finished." On some impulse or other, the woman squared her shoulders and drew a deep breath. To the man, it somehow seemed like a sigh.

"Everybody gets a year older each year," the man said suddenly, as if to soothe the woman. "Everything's all right. If we can go on living like this, there's nothing to complain about. It's not as if we had any great hopes. . . . Isn't that so, O-Chiyo? If I can live like this, I'm perfectly happy."

"That may be so, but we can't even go on living like this much longer. Already . . ."

"Already? What do you mean?"

"What, you ask. Because we are almost the same age. Even if I wanted to work, the customers . . ." Noticing the shadow moving around on the laundry platform, the woman abruptly lowered her voice. The man, crawling out of the bedding, said: "If it comes to that, I'm a man, after all. I'm not just living off you. You have no respect for me—I'm not good for very much in life, so no matter what people think I can't help it. But it's not as if I've been doing nothing like this without thinking about the future. As you get older, you're always thinking about the future. That's why, to this day, I've never wasted a cent of your earnings. You must know that yourself. Isn't that so, O-Chiyo?"

Although speaking in such a low voice that it was almost a murmur, the man put a strong emphasis into every syllable. Coming up right behind the woman, and even gripping her hands, he went on: "Don't you like me anymore? Already?"

"That kind of thing . . . What are you saying, all of a sudden?" As if surprised at him, the woman placed his hands over her breasts.

There was a sound of a door sliding open, and then the heavy sound of the woman who had been outside on the laundry platform stepping down onto the wooden floor. A moment later, the noon siren went off. As if changing her mind, the woman sat up.

"Let's not talk about that sort of thing. Eh, you? Please go to the post office for me later on."

"Yes. I'll go right now. . . . I'll go before I've had my breakfast." Getting to his feet, the man put on a sham silk padded garment with a haori over it that had been hung up on the wall. From downstairs, a man's voice called:

"Nakajima-san, phonecall."

"Yes. Thank you." Seeing that the woman was still in her sleeping dress without having even put on an under-sash yet, the man, his hand on the door, asked: "Is it all right if I answer it?"

"Yes. I've told the houses I do business with that I have a younger brother."

The man soon came back upstairs. "It's the Yoshizawa. They say to come right away."

"Ah, so?" Picking up the man's narrow obi, which had fallen to the floor, the woman put it on. Taking a cake of soap and a towel from the mirror-stand, she went downstairs. The man, taking a small aluminum pot from the tea shelf placed in the ornamental alcove, poured into it a bottle of milk, which had been standing in the corridor, and began to boil it. There were phonecalls at all hours of the night and day, and often there was no time even for a bowl of rice. The woman would go out, having fortified herself with hot milk or a raw egg. By the time the milk had begun to simmer, the woman, her hair done up and even her neck powder on, humming through her nose, came upstairs and seated herself at the mirror-stand.

"Ju–chan, have some. I ate late last night, so I don't need anything."

"Really? You have a very strange constitution. How can you not eat?"

"Ever since I was a child, I've almost never had three square meals a day. And yet, I don't like to drink and I don't care for soup either. . . . It saves money, doesn't it?"

"It certainly does. And you don't smoke . . ." The man watched as the woman's face in the mirror, under the movement of her fingers applying the makeup, grew instantly younger, as if it were the face of a different person. The wrinkles at the corners of the eyes, the freckles, were stroked away by the white face powder, the colorless lips took on the lipstick's ruby hue, the eyes sparkled in the round face with its narrow chin. Not only did it now appear more lively, it seemed somehow a modern face that even foreign clothes would become. The small compact body, when seen from behind, with its gracefully sloping shoulders and slender torso, set off all the more the heavy-fleshed thighs. As she sat there with one leg raised, O–Chiyo gave off the oppressive seductiveness of a woman in her prime. The man, satisfied that although she had turned thirty-six this year O–Chiyo still possessed that kind of powerful glamor, took courage at the thought that she could go on working for another four or five years. As he did so, a sense of shame and despair that had lain latent of late began to stir in him, so that despite himself he felt it strange that he had fallen this low in life. When human beings became this debased, it was the end. Not only his own feelings, but the mental state of O–Chiyo seemed strange to him. He'd become unable to clearly understand them. With what feelings had O–Chiyo come to be living with a feckless man like himself these past months and years? Most likely, without knowing it herself, habituated by now to life as an unlicensed prostitute, she had come to think even of shameful things as not shameful. No doubt, from time to time, she had had thoughts of changing to another line of work. But the fact of her having gone no further than grade school would make it difficult to find work even as a shopclerk or an office employee. Even if she did get a job, the salary doled out to one who had once practiced an illicit trade would be derisory. Probably she felt that in the whole world there was no profession suited to her lowly status other than this shameful calling, which at least she was familiar with. At the same time, contemplating the loneliness of a woman's lot, she must have felt the need of someone, no matter how feckless, whom she designated her lord and master, her companion in life. There was no other way to interpret the situation.

Noticing that the milk was on the boil, the man took the pot off the brazier and poured the milk into a glass. Just then completing her makeup, the woman changed into a padded silk garment with a "flying" pattern on a purple ground, an embroidered Nagoya sash, and a gardenia-colored haori of expensive twill. Completing this outfit with a white shawl and a scarlet handbag, she seated herself again at the mirror-stand to put the last touches on her face.

TWO

AFTER O-Chiyo had gone out, Jukichi made a combined breakfast and lunch of the leftover milk and a soft-boiled egg. When he had opened the window and put away his bedding, the cafe waitress (Ito by name) who rented the front part of the second floor, a haori thrown over her lined night kimono worn next to the skin and sticky with grime and makeup from her neck, looked in from the corridor.

"Nakajima-san . . . Oh, has your wife already gone out?"

"Is there something I can do for you?" Nakajima seated himself by the window.

"About before, I'm sorry. While you were sleeping . . ." Leaning against the sliding door, she went on: "I'd like you to address an envelope for me. I apologize for asking, but it's got to be in a man's handwriting."

"Of course. That's an easy task. . . . To your lover's place?"

"Uh uh." The woman shook her head like a child. "To my patron's place. Next month is December. Unless I start badgering him now, the money won't come in time. Even begging isn't easy."

"No matter what it is, you have to work at it."

"I'm sick and tired of life as a waitress." Taking out some envelopes from her pocket, the woman handed them to Nakajima. As he wrote out the name and address for her, she went on: "Nakajima-san, I'd like to ask your wife about joining the housekeepers' association. How about it, Nakajima-san? Perhaps it's something I can do. The kind of housekeeper your wife is doesn't have to cook rice like an ordinary housekeeper."

Nakajima did not like to be questioned too deeply about what O-Chiyo did. Merely nodding, he wrote out the same name on four or five envelopes. Sometime before, after consulting with him, O-Chiyo, in order to conceal her shady profession, had let it be known that as a temporary housekeeper she went out on call to any place the association sent her to. When, now and then, she stayed overnight, that was because she'd been hired for a banquet or some other entertainment at a distant villa.

Handing back the envelopes to the woman, Nakajima said: "Housekeeper, nothing—she's really a sort of high-class day maid. She's always saying how if she were only young, she'd like to be a waitress. She envies you."

"Then, no matter what it is, it's not that interesting. Thanks for doing the envelopes."

"I'll drop in at your cafe for the reward."

"Please do. We serve doughnuts. I'll give you some tea."

Shortly after the woman left, Nakajima, putting the post office savings passbook in his pocket, went downstairs. The house fronted on a back street, lined with retail shops, in Shiba Sakuragawa-cho. The glass shop, open to the street the full length of its eighteen-foot frontage, was half an entryway where plate glass was stored. The owner, a man of about fifty with a mustache, his bucktoothed spouse, and their fourteen- or fifteen-year-old son who was by way of a shopboy, lived here. Passing through the six-mat room at the foot of the stairs where the family was having its lunch, excusing himself, Nakajima stepped out the kitchen door. Walking along the alley, he presently emerged on an avenue and made his way toward a trolley stop. The branch post office where O-Chiyo had her account was in Tanimachi, at the base of the slope in Azabu-Roppongi. That was because for more than a year, until moving this spring to Sakuragawa-cho, she'd rented a room in an alley near there. One day, however, from their second-floor windows, O-Chiyo had seen and been seen by one of her former patrons, who had moved into the house with lattice doors diagonally opposite. She had met him two or three times in an assignation house in Ikenohata, she said, and lest her secret profession come to be known among the neighbors, she had immediately moved to her present room. Although meaning to transfer her account to a nearby branch, she'd ended up leaving it where it was.

In addition to the twelve yen of the room rent, Nakajima had promised to chip in five yen for the telephone as well as paying for the cost of every call. That made seventeen yen. Calculating O-Chiyo's tailor bill and general end-of-the-month expenses, he withdrew about fifty yen. Quickly returning to the trolley stop, he found seven or eight people waiting on the usually deserted pavement. There was no sign of a trolley. Of late, Jukichi had almost never ventured out on a main thoroughfare during the day. Even the winter sunlight instantly dazzled him like that of summer. He had come out without his Inverness cape. The wind, cold and desolate, blew against him. Suddenly, he felt hungry. Anxious to avoid meeting any old friends or acquaintances these days, when he saw the crowd at the trolley stop gradually grow larger, Jukichi walked on toward the next stop, threading his way between telephone poles and sidewalk trees as if making a getaway.

When he'd gone as far as Tame-ike, from behind him, at last, a trolley car came along. It was full. A woman, barely slipping free of the press of people impatiently waiting to get on and people pushing their way off, glanced at Nakajima as she was about to pass him. "Nakajima-san?"

"Tama-chan. How have you been?" His tone unusually relaxed since it was not a male acquaintance, Nakajima looked her over. Age, twenty-seven or -eight. Over a purple haori, evidently readymade, an ordinary woolen shawl. Red lacquerware sandals, and a folded parasol.

"And Chiyoko-san? Is she all right?"

"Yes, she's fine."

"It's bad of me not to have visited you even once, but I didn't know where you were." Looking around her, the woman took advantage of the momentary lull in traffic and the deserted stop for a bit of chitchat. "Do you live in this neighborhood?"

"No, in Sakuragawa-cho . . . number eighteen. On the second floor of a glass seller's called Ota. It's not far from Toranomon, so if you like, do come by."

"If you don't mind the imposition . . . Actually, I'm looking for a room. I'm in Setagaya now. But the rooms around here are terribly expensive."

As they talked, the two were strolling along the back streets of Tame-ike.

"After that time, we didn't see anything of you. Even O-Chiyo thought that you'd probably left Tokyo. But you haven't altogether shaken the dust off your feet, have you?"

"I started to shake the dust off. I shook the dust off one foot, ha-ha."

"Are you still with your friend?"

"No. We broke up. This summer, we finally came to

an agreement and separated. And other things have happened. Last year, in the spring, the madam of the Nakanawa Club was arrested. I was rounded up too. After that, I was at loose ends for a month or so. But things went on the same with my friend, and there was nothing else I could do, so until just recently I've been working at a small cafe in Shibuya. It was busier than I thought, but it wasn't likely that two people could live on the tips alone. Although he'd agreed to everything, you know what my friend is like. I myself found it too much. We split everything we had. We even agreed on the money— a hundred yen. It was all done nice and proper through a go-between. So from now on, I'm working on my own. It'll be much more free and easy that way."

"Is that so? But have you really given him up? Won't you get back together soon?"

"Stop that. I may be a complete fool, but no man is going to live off . . ." the woman began, then, remembering Nakajima's relationship with O-Chiyo, abruptly changed her tone. "That's so, you know. If the man gave me understanding and sympathy . . . If he understood me like you, Nakajima-san—I'm a woman, and I would do anything for such a man. I would be happy to."

"But in the end you'd probably get tired of me. When the man has no self-respect at all . . . Isn't that so, Tama-chan? When we were living in the same house, somehow we never had this kind of talk. O-Chiyo, you know . . . I can't figure out why she wants to live with me. It gives me a strange feeling sometimes."

"Oh, come now, Na-san. What are you saying? At this late stage in the game, to suddenly . . ."

"I mentioned it because the subject came up. It's not that I'm particularly worried about it. But a woman's feelings, unless you ask her about them, it's like understanding without understanding . . ."

"That may be so. But it's the same for us women. You seem to understand a man's feelings, without understanding them. Oh, Na-san. Why wasn't my loverboy as mature and sympathetic as you?"

"Are you already wishing he'd come back?"

"No. That's over with. Next time, I'm going to look for a congenial lover, like you, Na-san."

"What do you mean, a congenial lover?"

"O-Chiyo told me about you. She says you like this sort of life. She says you talked her into it."

"Did O-Chiyo say that kind of thing? Ha-ha. But no matter how much I talked, if the woman herself hadn't wanted to, I couldn't have done it. We're birds of the same feather. That's why we're able to get along so well. There are reasons for that. There's a real story behind it. . . ."

At first, half-jokingly, Nakajima had said whatever had come to him, just as he'd been prompted. But somewhere along the way, he'd begun to feel an intimacy, an uncontrollable desire to tell, as far as his feelings took him, the story of half his lifetime, which ordinarily he was unable to talk about with anyone.

"It was while I was still a student, you know, Tama-chan? I . . ." he began to say. But just then O-Tama, spotting a room-to-let sign in the bay window of a house up an alley, interrupted him.

"Excuse me. I think I'll ask here." She had stopped short. Nakajima, his discourse broken off, looking as if he'd awoken from a dream, vaguely watched her from behind as O-Tama slid open the lattice door of the house opposite.

THREE

NAKAJIMA, or to call him by his personal name, Jukichi, had graduated from a private university in the sixth or seventh year of Taisho. During this period, thanks to the European War, the Japanese business world was at its most prosperous. Jukichi had no difficulty finding a position as the editor of a magazine put out by a certain firm by way of publicity. Although not particularly good at the job, he lacked sincerity and even tended to be late for work. He was fired after a year. But he had a reason, just then, for not having to worry about making a living. Whiling away the tedious days with such things as billiards and fishing, he also tried his hand at writing. But he had neither the enthusiasm nor the self-confidence to become a writer. Making his rejection in a newspaper short-story contest his farewell to literature, he gave up that diversion as if he'd forgotten all about it. Discarding, at one point or another, the five or six stories he'd taken the trouble to make clean copies of, he had retained just one piece, an autobiographical account he evidently found it hard to throw away. Even now, he kept it carefully stored away in an old briefcase in the clothes closet. On evenings when O-Chiyo was staying overnight somewhere, Jukichi often took out this old work and reread it.

This story related almost fact for fact Jukichi's life during the five or six years before and after his graduation, when he was living with a widow more than ten years older than himself.

The lady operated a billiards parlor in the Hirakawa section of Koji-machi. Accompanied by four or five student customers, she would often go to the movies or take strolls along the Ginza or in Asakusa Park. Jukichi was one of those invited on these outings. Every year in August, the widow closed up shop and went to the seashore at Kamakura to escape the heat. One summer, Jukichi followed her there and promptly became her lover. When the cool weather came and they returned to Tokyo, the widow immediately sold the billiards parlor and Jukichi left his boardinghouse. The pair rented a house together. Just at that time, Jukichi received word from his family in the country that they could no longer send him money for his academic expenses. Thanks to his liaison with the widow, however, Jukichi was able not only to complete his education without impediment but later, when he lost his job, to relax and enjoy himself.

Jukichi's family were proprietors of an inn in Niigata. Both his parents had died early, and his older brother had taken over the family headship. The inn did nothing but lose money, however, and debts simply piled up from year to year. Finally, having settled his financial affairs, the brother had emigrated with his family to Seoul and was strenuously seeking his fortune there. Jukichi, in his reply saying that student though he was here was a fine opportunity to support himself and that they were not to worry, moved in with the widow.

At that time, after his graduation, Jukichi was working at his editor's job. One day, the widow, who always waited for Jukichi's return, was out of the house when he got back and did not get back herself until nearly midnight. Her breath reeked of sake. When Jukichi, in the excess of his mortification, upbraided her in a tearful voice, the woman, as if soothing a child, said: "Ju-chan. Please forgive me. You can't hold your liquor, so today I went to have a little meal with a friend who likes sake. It was bad of me to come back so late, and I'm truly sorry. You needn't worry, Ju-chan. I'll never be unfaithful to you."

Then, displaying such passion that even though Jukichi tried to suspect her he could not, she made it up to him in bed by way of apology.

Nearly half a year passed. One morning Jukichi, as usual leaving the late-sleeping widow upstairs in bed, was sitting on the threshold putting on his shoes. Just then the postman tossed in right under his nose a bundle of printed matter, apparently magazines. Taking them with him, Jukichi set out for work. After boarding a trolley, as he began to tear through the half-wrapper, he noticed a letter inserted between the rolled-up magazines. It was addressed to Taneko (the widow's name), and the sender's name was also a woman's. But Jukichi, that instant, felt a kind of premonition. As soon as he got to the office, he skillfully pried open the envelope and read the letter. In a man's handwriting completely different from the super-scription, its every line and word were such as to bring Jukichi's feelings to the boil. Among them, such phrases as "so, looking forward with pleasure to next Wednes-day," "please don't forget that day yourself," and "at the usual time" pierced Jukichi's heart with especial sharp-ness. He could tell when "next Wednesday" was by look-ing at the calendar, but what was "the usual time"? Jukichi thought of a plan. To investigate the widow Taneko's con-duct, rather than something like following her around, the quickest way would be to have a private detective who specialized in such matters look into her antecedents. Making up his mind, Jukichi set aside the unspent portion of that month's salary as a payment to the detective agency.

Taneko, it turned out, was not a widow. Ten years ago, she had been the concubine of an industrialist who had hanged himself in prison where he was serving a sentence for breach of trust. Previously, she'd been a private tutor in the household of the industrialist. Perhaps the personal property and real estate presently in her name were part of the wealth that had been legally squirreled away by the criminal before his arrest. Moreover, among the men whom Taneko was currently having relations with, the detective agency discovered, were a *biwa** instructor in the Chikuzen mode, a New Method actor, and a traditional painter.

Before long, however, Jukichi was dismissed by the company. About a year later, he was privileged to hear from the lips of the lady herself, with nothing held back, detailed accounts that were even more circumstantial than the detective agency's report. Whether she thought she could not much longer conceal her indiscretions, or whether to draw out her lover's sympathy, Taneko even made bold to say this: "Ju-chan, for more than ten years, from when I was nineteen until I was thirty, I was the plaything of a really terrible person. I wonder how I ever stood it. I'm impressed despite myself that I did. I made up my mind, during that time, that when I got my freedom, I would do what I pleased, to try to make up for my lost youth. So, if you sympathize with me and feel sorry for me, please overlook it if I go around and have a little fun. No matter how bad I've been, I've never even dreamed of leaving you and taking up with another man.

*Japanese lute (tr. note).

I'm just playing around. Deep in my heart, I'm absolutely faithful to you. To prove it, hasn't that man, and after him that man, haven't they all been married men? Since you've been living with me, I have never once fooled around with a man with whom there might be complications afterward. If it'll give you peace of mind, I'll put anything you like in writing."

Jukichi, when he'd quietly thought over what Taneko had said, realized for the first time that he was virtually a male concubine who had been purchased by a lascivious female ex-concubine. To put what she had said another way, she was telling him: "You are a nice university graduate and won't make any trouble. I can live with you with an easy mind. Other men, different from you, are worldly-wise and might have an eye on my money. That's why I don't let them into the house, keep them at a distance, and meet them outside. I know exactly what I'm doing, so if you'll just go along with it without worrying too much about it, everything will be all right." That was what it amounted to. Feeling a humiliation he'd never before experienced, Jukichi made up his mind to leave the woman's house. Then again, however, he quietly thought over his position. In the nearly twelve months that had gone by since he'd lost his job, the energy to start looking for another job had slackened in him, accustomed as he'd become to a life of idleness. Even if he went back to the country, his family there had long since broken up. Along with the realization of just how difficult it was to make a living, Jukichi was clearly aware that if he could only swallow the insult and resign himself to his present circumstances, he would lack for neither money nor sex.

If Jukichi were to continue living off Taneko, he would

first of all have to rid himself completely of a man's self-respect.

In this world, there are many persons who, to follow the road to success, have themselves adopted into wealthy families or marry into politically powerful families. Even among famous people, highly praised in today's world, this sort of thing is not unusual. Compared to them, Jukichi did not have that much to be ashamed of. To be paid for by a woman, to live the life of a drone: compared to the official who takes bribes and wallows in luxury, it is as nothing. Drawing his examples from others' gossip, the events of society, and what he saw and heard every day, Jukichi found a way to anesthetize his conscience and buttress his self-respect.

In his autobiographical short story, Jukichi had described his struggles with himself and made them the justification for his conduct. Apparently he had had trouble with the title of the story. The characters on the title page of the manuscript had been rubbed out any number of times and remained illegible.

FOUR

EVEN afterward, two or three times a month, Taneko would go out in the afternoon and not come back until late at night. At the beginning of each month, she would visit the grave of her benefactor, who had even shared his wealth with her, and at the end of the month she went to the bank where her money and promissory notes were deposited. In addition, there were shopping trips to the department stores. Even for a short distance, she would send for an expensive taxicab to pick her up at her door. Jukichi, already inured to his lot, did not fret himself about such things as much as he had at first. In fact, as time passed it gradually became clear that Taneko's conduct, even tacitly acquiesced in, had no harmful influence on Jukichi's own career. Not only that, but through an introduction of a friend of Taneko's he was hired as a publicity writer by a real estate company, and so was able to earn his living again, albeit a meager one. He now felt much calmer about his situation than he had before.

The life of the pair, as they moved from Akasaka where they'd first rented a house to the Shiba Park area, and from there to Higashi-Nakano, in the eyes of those who knew nothing about them, seemed enviably fortunate and tranquil.

At the time of the Tokyo Earthquake, Taneko was forty-five and Jukichi just thirty-three. Taneko, who made herself up and dressed as a younger woman, and the swarthy, diminutive Jukichi, who had been prematurely gray since his twenties, no longer seemed that far apart in age even when they sat side by side. Taneko, her face caked with white rice powder and cheek rouge, her hair done in the then popular "ear-covering" style, wearing a kimono with a "flying" pattern and a flashy, embroidered gold brocade half-collar, would utter peals of shrill, noisy laughter. At her side, dressed in a sober mosquito splash–pattern kimono of Oshima pongee with a matching haori, Jukichi would significantly clear his throat and pass his hand over his gradually balding forehead. They seemed a respectable couple, rather than a pair of lovers twelve or thirteen years apart in age.

When the earthquake struck that first day of September, Jukichi, showing a client around some lots for sale in Shita Meguro, was in no danger at all. Taneko, however, was caught while shopping at the Shirokiya Department Store. Rushing outside in a panic, jostled and buffeted by the crowd, now walking, now running, Taneko lost her sandals and then injured her foot on some sharp object. Toward nightfall, assisted by passers-by, she finally made it back to the house.

The cut in her foot presently healed. That winter, however, she caught a cold that developed into peritonitis. Shortly after entering the Red Cross Hospital, she took a turn for the worse. On the doctor's advice and by the patient's request, two relatives—one from Mito, the other from Sendai—neither of whom Jukichi had met up to now, were summoned to the hospital. When Taneko died on the evening of the next day, a discussion immediately arose between the relatives concerning the disposition of Taneko's assets. (The relative from Mito, a middle-school teacher, said he was Taneko's older brother; the one from Sendai, a local lawyer, said he was her uncle.)

Although they ransacked the house, they could not find the deceased person's will. It was therefore decided that the two relatives would divide the assets, leaving the left-overs—the approximately five thousand yen in the bank and the furniture and clothes, as well as the accessories—to Jukichi. Although Jukichi protested, the lawyer-uncle explained to him that legally he was not entitled to complain. The brother from Mito, an instructor in Chinese composition with a third degree in judo, interrogating Jukichi as to how he had wormed his way into Taneko's house, displayed a moral energy that stopped just short of taking Jukichi to court. Jukichi had no choice but to reluctantly agree to whatever they did. In school, Jukichi had once gotten into a fight with a boy from Mito, who'd threatened him with a dagger in a plain wooden sheath. Ever since then, he had been extraordinarily afraid of people from Mito.

After the funeral, the two relatives departed with a somewhat triumphant air. Left behind all by himself, feeling as if he'd awakened from a long, long dream, Jukichi wondered what he should do. Nothing presented itself.

"Master, I've cooked some rice . . ." a voice said. Surprised, Jukichi looked around. Without his noticing, it had begun to grow dark. The room was dusky. A lonely wind stirred the trees in the garden. When he'd stood up and turned on the light, Jukichi saw at his knees the face of a girl who had brought in a small supper table. She was not the young woman they usually employed. He realized that she was the temporary housekeeper they'd hired the day before the deathwatch, when they were short of help.

Her age, at a glance, seemed to be twenty-five or -six. Although she was not especially good-looking, the extraordinary whiteness of her skin, her bright, clear eyes, and her conspicuously long, thick eyelashes enlivened the features of her round face. Her voice, too, like that of a girl of sixteen or seventeen, had an indefinable innocence about it. Jukichi noticed it for the first time.

"Will you serve me some, then?" He held out his rice bowl. Without appearing particularly embarrassed, the girl replied: "I've forgotten the tray. Please forgive me." Serving the rice, she went on: "Perhaps you can't eat anything. I didn't know what to make for you."

Outside the room, the housemaid began to roll open the rain shutters of the veranda.

"No, this is good. It's delicious." Jukichi drank at a single gulp half the soup with a poached egg in it. During the three or four days before and after the funeral, there had been no time for a leisurely meal. Only now beginning to realize how hungry he was, he could not actually taste the food very well. The girl, seeming happier and happier for being praised, said: "You must eat a lot, now. Because your fatigue will come out all at once."

"O-Chiyo-san. Is that your only name? Evidently you've been through funerals yourself, O-Chiyo-san."

"There haven't been any in my family, but I've worked at funerals."

"Have you been doing this for long?"

"It's still only a short time. I'd been working since before the Earthquake, then I took a little vacation, and I started again last month."

"You weren't hurt in the Earthquake? And your parents . . . ?"

"No. They live outside the city. . . . They're in the country."

"You haven't gotten married yet? Somehow you look as if you had."

157

"Do I look as if I had? Ha-ha."

"You mean you were married, and it didn't go well?"

"Yes. I've learned my lesson. It's easier working in other people's houses."

"But that can't go on forever, surely. Working in other people's houses. You're not yet at an age where you have to be pessimistic about your prospects. If you look, there are bound to be plenty of men."

"That's very kind of you. But marriage is something that's not there when it seems to be."

"Or it's there when it seems not to be. It depends on how you look at it."

"Well then. If there's a promising candidate, I'll ask for your help."

"O-Chiyo-san. How old are you? Twenty-five or -six?"

"I'm glad I look so young. Actually, I'm already twenty-eight."

After the girl, smiling pleasantly, had removed the supper table, she came back directly for the rice server, chatted a while with Jukichi, and went back to the kitchen.

There was nothing for Jukichi to do but go to bed. Although thinking that in addition to disposing of the deceased Taneko's clothing and precious jewelry, he would have to immediately sell this house and learn to live from now solely on his own salary, he felt not the slightest wish to begin. Letting the fire in the brazier die down into ashes, his arms folded, he vaguely watched the play of shadows on the wall. Presently the housemaid came in with some green tea.

"What about O-Chiyo-san? Tell her she can go to bed."

"Yes." Shortly after the maid had left the room,

O-Chiyo, bringing a hot water bottle, slid open the paper door.

"Oh. I thought the bedding had been laid out. Forgive me."

"But the master didn't say anything." The housemaid went off again with a sulky expression. O-Chiyo, taking down the bedclothes from the closet, after spreading out the sheets, began to take out a pillow. Not knowing which of the two identical pillows stuffed with buckwheat chaff was the man's, she started to say: "Master, which of these . . ." But then, quickly realizing by Jukichi's silence that she'd said the wrong thing, she blushed slightly. Taking out a pillow without having ascertained which was which, she placed it at the head of the sheets. Then she knelt formally on the mat.

As if he'd been waiting for that, Jukichi abruptly put his arms around her from behind.

"No. You mustn't . . ." Her voice unexpectedly low, O-Chiyo writhed in an attempt to get free of Jukichi. "Please stop. The maid will come . . ."

Jukichi, as if brought to his senses by the mention of the maid, relaxed his grip and looked into O-Chiyo's face. He'd thought that O-Chiyo would say something angry or stamp on the mat and storm out of the room. Instead, merely saying: "It's not right. You're just playing around. If you do it again, I'll scream for help," she took what she guessed to be Jukichi's nightclothes from the closet, and, laying them by the pillow, went around to the foot of the bedding to put in the hot water bottle. Jukichi, observing her closely, had the thought that O-Chiyo was a little too good-looking for a housekeeper and must have come up against this sort of thing often. That was why she was surprisingly calm about it. There might be trouble later on, but he would deal with that when it occurred. His feelings grew more and more disorderly.

"Sleep well." Putting both hands to the mat, O-Chiyo bowed her head to him. As she was about to leave the room, Jukichi called her back in an agitated voice.

"Please don't go. I won't do anything. Somehow I feel unbearably lonely."

FIVE

ACCORDING to O-Chiyo's story, she was the daughter of a shipping agent in Nishi-funabori, on the Nakagawa Embankment. Longing for the city, she'd ignored her parents' advice and run away from home to an acquaintance in Tokyo, where she went to work as a maid in a mansion in Takanawa. That was in the spring of 1912, the year the era name changed from Meiji to Taisho. That summer, practitioners of various strange arts were holding forth every evening in Shibahara of Marunouchi. People would gather in great numbers to watch the faith-healing ceremonies. O-Chiyo, sneaking out late at night with the houseboy and the rickshaw man, would set out for the pitch-dark Marunouchi district. One night, however, she was caught and reprimanded by a policeman, and sent back to the country by her employers. By then, O-Chiyo was already pregnant. The baby was a girl, and O-Chiyo's aged mother undertook to bring it up. Saying she at least wanted to earn enough for its upkeep, O-Chiyo returned to Tokyo and entered service again. Three or four years later, through a suitable intermediary, she married into the family of a sundries dealer. Not long after, her mother in the country died. Confiding the circumstances to her husband, O-Chiyo took the child into her care. But things went well for barely a year. After her husband's parents and brothers had descended upon them from the country, the household fell apart in chaos. The shop had to close down, and poverty was upon them.

O-Chiyo had disliked rough, dirty work since girlhood days in her parents' house, and from the start her heart had not been in this marriage. Having a talk, she and her husband agreed to separate. Luckily, she was able to place the child for adoption by neighbors at their own request. On her own now, O-Chiyo diverted herself with a series of maid's jobs and then signed on with a housekeepers' agency.

The next morning, Jukichi, after he'd sent the maid out on errands, had O-Chiyo open the drawers and doors of the chest where Taneko's clothes were stored. Inhaling with evident pleasure the smell of camphor, O-Chiyo exclaimed in wonder each time she pulled open a drawer.

"Master, you say all this splendid clothing is mine now? Master, it must be a lie."

"Why would I tell you a lie? If you don't need them, I'll go ahead and sell them. In that chest of drawers, there are rings and other jewelry. They've been divided between her relatives. You can look at them, if you like."

"Yes. Please let me see them. If I were to take a nice leisurely look at just the clothes, it would take me all day."

O-Chiyo's face was flushed and her eyes bloodshot, as if she were having a rush of blood to the head. Excitedly taking out the rings and wristwatches from their boxes, she tried them on and took them off, each time breathing a deep sigh.

"There's no hurry about the division of the jewelry. If you don't lose anything, you can wear it for two or three days."

"Oh, you—if it had been before the Earthquake, I would have liked to wear this ring and walk around in the Mitsukoshi Department Store. But now there's no place to go."

"Ha–ha." Laughing despite himself, Jukichi nevertheless felt a strange, pitying melancholy come over him at
O–Chiyo's excessive happiness. Was this what women
were like?

Right after lunch, O–Chiyo went off to cancel her contract with the housekeepers' agency. Jukichi dismissed the
maid, who had been hired while Taneko was alive. Then,
together with O–Chiyo, who'd returned at lamplighting
time, all but holding hands with her, he went off to the
neighborhood bathhouse.

For some time after the Earthquake, profits in the real
estate business were extraordinarily good. Even Jukichi,
who worked for a land company, received unprecedented
bonuses. The Kabuki Theater had just been rebuilt, and
Jukichi attended performances with O–Chiyo decked out
in Taneko's finery. During the hot weather, they would
go off to Hakone for three days or so. Having sold the
house in the suburbs, they moved to Yarai-cho in Ushigome. Every night, they went around hand in hand looking at the stalls set up at night on the Kagura Slope. Their
life, like that of newlyweds, was a happy one.

However, this happiness, as general economic conditions worsened, was gradually destroyed. In the spring
of the second year of Showa, nearly every bank in Tokyo
closed its doors. The five thousand yen that was Jukichi's
bequest from Taneko was lost at this time. Next, the
company that Jukichi worked for abruptly went under.
By now, every one of Taneko's precious keepsakes had
long since been surreptitiously sold off.

Although secretly appalled at this sudden descent into
hard times, Jukichi invented a story for O–Chiyo's bene-
fit that the company would soon reopen after a financial
consolidation, and that she was to be patient. Meanwhile,

he frittered away the days. As the last day of each month drew near, O-Chiyo had to pawn one after the other Taneko's articles of clothing that she had so rejoiced in taking possession of.

"Ju-chan, how would it be if we rented a room somewhere? It would be much cheaper than owning a house." It was O-Chiyo herself, one day, who brought the subject up.

Jukichi, although he had secretly waited for this, without so much as a "Hm. Is that so?," displayed his usual calm demeanor. "The company will probably work things out before long. Actually, just yesterday, I was summoned to the director's house. . . ."

"If things go back to what they were, wouldn't it be better to rent a house then? We shouldn't try to live above our means. Also, you know—except for my clothes for this season, everything's gone."

"Is that so? I hadn't realized that. I've done something truly unforgivable." Putting on an expression as if he'd learned of this for the first time, Jukichi continued: "From now on, I'll take my own things to the pawnshop. You should stop selling yours."

"But a man has to keep up appearances. If it's come to this, I don't care what I wear." O-Chiyo's voice was tearful.

"It's truly unforgivable." Jukichi, as if blinking back his tears, covertly observed the woman's manner. He'd thought from the first that when the supply of articles for pawning was exhausted, he would have to hear what O-Chiyo had to say and carry out his "final resolution" accordingly. This "final resolution," whether it meant O-Chiyo's becoming a shopgirl, a waitress, or a housekeeper again for the necessities of life, was bound to endlessly dog their life together, he thought.

Flowers in the Shade

In his student days—from the time when, unlike today, there had not been many cafes and dance halls—Jukichi had realized that he was a man who would put up with any humiliation to gain a woman's favor. During the seven or eight years when he had ingratiated himself with the lady proprietor of a luxurious billiards hall and was living a lewd and licentious existence, Jukichi had even experienced pleasure in the humiliations he endured from the woman. Women loved best the man who let them inflict whatever high-handed cruelty they pleased. Unless they could despise the man and keep him under their thumb, or unless on the contrary they were abused by the man, they were not satisfied. From his own experience, Jukichi had confirmed that they would not leave off desiring either one or the other of these extremes.

What would O-Chiyo do? She had lived with him for more than four years, and already was over thirty. During that time, she had been given everything that women want. Probably she felt both a debt of gratitude and a lingering affection for him. Furthermore, in view of her age, there was no fear that she would cast him off. Seeing that she hadn't left him even though for more than half a year he'd been selling off her clothes, that much was certain. From early on in this relationship, Jukichi had made certain calculations in his heart.

Jukichi, aware that for these last three or four years cafe waitresses had been making a lot of money, wanted O-Chiyo to be a waitress. But he was afraid that if he broached the matter himself, he would be thought heartless by the woman. He hoped to handle O-Chiyo in such a way that she would suggest it of her own accord. Paying no attention to his attempts to stop her, she would boldly go ahead and do it.

Since O-Chiyo had proposed that they sell the house

and rent a room, Jukichi felt that he'd already accomplished half his purpose. After they'd moved to the second floor of a residential shop in Iida-cho, Jukichi reasoned that if he stayed home all the time it would give the woman no time for leisurely reflection. When women, in uncertain situations, boldly carried out decisions superior in resolve to those even of men, it was not the result of consideration and judgment. Generally, it was from the impulse of the moment. This impulse, Jukichi thought, often came from their having endured loneliness and boredom. He decided to stay out of the house for irregular periods. Of course, it was also to visit acquaintances from the defunct land company and to ask for a job that he did so.

Once, he called on an ex-colleague of fifty who in the intervening year had found work as an insurance salesman. After some desultory chitchat, the man said this kind of thing: "You're different from the likes of me. You've still got it easy. Your woman is young and good-looking. If you're stone-broke, she'll go to work for you."

"Now that we've sunk this low, we can't afford to give a damn about appearances," Jukichi replied. "Actually, I've thought about sending her out as a waitress. But it's a bit awkward having to suggest the thing myself."

"What's so bad about it? There are all types in the world. To take an extreme example, there are husbands who even make their wives become rich men's concubines. At the real estate agency, do you remember that salesman Nojima, the tall one with the buckteeth? His wife worked as a clerk at a stockbroker's and had a relationship with the manager. Thanks to Nojima's turning a blind eye to it, she finally wormed enough money out of the man to open a cafe in Ningyo-cho."

"Is that so? I never knew that. It's a familiar story, but what do you think happens? Does the man secretly put the woman up to it, or does she start doing it on her own, and then he pretends he doesn't know?"

"It's not like other things. If you encouraged them or told them to do it, it probably wouldn't go well. A woman who's been pushed into being a waitress or a geisha cannot be said to be the right person in the right place. Unless she's gone ahead and done it without listening to the opposition of her family, she won't be very good at it, they say."

Another time, when Jukichi was visiting somebody else, this person said to him: "Why don't you forget about finding some low-paying job, Nakajima? Why don't you find yourself some rich widow? Since you're the sort of man women like, you'd be sure to find something."

SIX

On her way back from the corner grocery store, O–Chiyo met someone whom she hadn't seen in so long that she couldn't remember the person even when her name was called out. She hadn't forgotten that the man was a householder whom she'd gone to work for as a temporary housekeeper before the Earthquake, but she could not remember his name.

"How did you ever remember my name?"

The man, keeping an eye on the passers-by, said to O–Chiyo: "I'd like you to come again for a while. What's your phone number?"

"Right now, I'm no longer at the agency. One of my relatives is sick, and I've come to help out," O–Chiyo said evasively. Before, when O–Chiyo had gone to this man's house from the agency, she'd been seduced despite herself and ended up staying about a month. In addition to her regular daily pay, she'd received twenty or thirty yen.

"I'm still at the same address. Kobinata-suidocho . . . you remember it, don't you? Just a day or two would be good. When you get a chance, just come over. It's rude of me, but here's your carfare." The man pressed two or three 50-sen coins into O–Chiyo's hand. Looking back at her, he turned off into an alley across the way.

Lately, O–Chiyo had been cudgeling her brains as to how to pay at least part of the interest on certain articles of clothing at the pawnshop that she was determined not to forfeit. Now that she had been stopped in the street unexpectedly and even been given carfare by the man, it occurred to her that she might raise the money simply by paying him a visit. That day, as it happened, Jukichi had gone out to apply for a job as a traveling salesman he'd seen advertised in the paper and would not get back until late in the evening. O-Chiyo prepared supper for him and, leaving word with the people downstairs, was on her way to Kobinata-suidocho before she knew it. Although it was after ten when she got back, Jukichi didn't get back until a half-hour later, so that that night's affair was buried in secrecy.

One day, after Jukichi had gone out, O-Chiyo was spreading her nightclothes to dry on the windowsill of their second-floor room, when a voice called up to her from the street. "Ma'am. Nakajima-san's wife." It was a woman of about fifty, apparently a widow, who, shortly after O-Chiyo had moved here, had struck up a free and easy acquaintance with her in the neighborhood bath-house. On their way back from the baths, she would invite O-Chiyo up for a cup of tea. She even went so far as to say: "If you're ever in a tight spot and need some money, I'll lend it to you. Without a promissory note or anything." O-Chiyo, although thinking she'd like to avail herself of the offer after consultation with Jukichi, was unable to say so. The matter had rested there. She hadn't gone to visit the woman, nor had the woman come to visit her.

Previously, in the Sakashita section of Otsuka, and before that in Negishi and before that in Takanawa, this old woman had been frequently arrested on charges of running a prostitution agency. She was an old hand in the trade. She had moved to this neighborhood at about the same time that O-Chiyo had. From many years' experience, she possessed a power of observation that could tell at a glance whether a woman could be led astray or not. Especially in the women's bath, from the way a woman took off her clothes and put them back on, she could not only tell straightaway what that woman's past and present circumstances were but also unerringly judge whether she was the sort who would appeal to men. O-Chiyo had caught this old woman's eye. She eyed her as a jewel, ideal even from the point of view of age for the satiated client who had developed a taste for the repulsive.

It was nearly three months since they'd first spoken to each other. Observing O-Chiyo's clothes, which she'd worn ever since that time, the old woman saw that although of superior material they were worn threadbare around the sleeve-openings and the hems of the skirts. When O-Chiyo came to the bathhouse, the old woman noted that she wore them next to the skin and that her loincloth was a crude, unbecoming affair that she never changed. By these appearances alone, the old woman judged that the time was ripe to make her proposition. She had come by on her way to the baths to sound out O-Chiyo while getting a look at her place. In the second-floor room, with its tattered paper doors and dirty mats, everything, from the chest of drawers and the brazier to the writing table and its cushions, had formerly belonged to the wealthy Taneko. As such, it was too good for the likes of O-Chiyo. The old woman, much thrown out in her original calculations and suspicious of the couple's circumstances, nonetheless surmised that having fallen this low in the world O-Chiyo would be open to suggestions from the mere fact of having lived well in the past.

"Is your husband out every day?" She started by saying this kind of thing.

"Yes. He's never in. He's been out of work lately."

"It must be lonely, keeping house all by yourself. I don't have a maid myself and have nothing to do. I don't even sew. So when I occasionally visit people, I end up staying a long time."

"It's different for women. They can't even stroll around on their own."

"Ma'am, wouldn't you like to go work somewhere, half for the fun of it? It would give you something to do."

"Unless you've graduated from girls' school, it's no good. And I'm already too old to get a job. I've never worked with a lot of people up to now. Every so often, I look at the newspaper advertisements, but I don't believe I could even work as a cafe waitress."

"If you truly wanted the job, I'm sure that wherever you went you'd be hired on the spot. However . . . this is just between us, but even if you were so inclined, your husband might not approve."

"As long as we can get along one way or another, that might be so . . . but when you're down and out, you can't afford to care about appearances. It's you, Auntie, so I'm telling you this, but my husband . . . well, he's been out of work since the summer. Even the little money we had has gradually disappeared."

"That's truly how it is. You always think: 'He'll come back soon, he'll come back soon.' It's that feeling of waiting, of worrying, that's so unpleasant. When you're at home by yourself like this, come over and we'll have a carefree chat, even about foolish things. It'll be good for you to divert yourself. As I mentioned earlier, if it's not too much, I can lend you money anytime, so please feel free to ask me. There's such a thing as comradeship between women, too."

"Oh, thank you. But I could never impose upon you, on such a short acquaintance."

"Yes, it's true a big loan would get us both into difficulty. But in any household there are little expenses one can't mention even to one's husband. If you have just a little credit, you can get the money anywhere. Even the most respectable housewives have this kind of problem."

"That's so, I suppose. But if your credit is good, you can get money without any trouble. But if you have no hope of paying it back, there's no way of getting any."

Now, the old woman thought, was the time to bring up her ultimate subject. "Ma'am, it's a strange thing to be talking about, but . . . let's be perfectly frank with each other," she began, keeping a sharp eye on O-Chiyo's expression and overall demeanor. "This is strictly between us. If you'd like to be a waitress . . . if the customer wanted to go somewhere and have some fun—you know what I mean? It would be like tossing yourself into the rapids and trusting to fate. When your husband's out, I'll get word to you secretly, so just come over to my place. . . ."

O-Chiyo, looking fixedly at the old woman's face, gradually flushed scarlet. Then, without saying a word, she lowered her eyes. The evening before, she had taken advantage of Jukichi's absence to go out again to Kobinata-suidocho. Not only did she know perfectly well what the old woman was getting at, but she felt as if she had been seen through, even about last night's business. That was why she'd unconsciously blushed.

When O-Chiyo, without either growing angry or bursting into tears, merely swayed slightly to one side and turned red, the old woman decided that her words had been sufficiently understood. To her mind, O-Chiyo's blush signified an acquiescence even deeper than that of a spoken "yes."

"Well, then, ma'am. Thank you for putting up with me." Saying this, the old woman quietly took her leave.

 SEVEN

"O-CHIYO, from now I'm going to work at home. I'm just wearing out shoe leather by walking around every day. It's no use. I've given up. From now on, I stay home." Taking off just his jacket, Jukichi leaned back against the table. Cupping the back of his head in his hands, he flung out both legs.

"If you work at home, I can help you too," O-Chiyo said, starting to make some tea.

"If it's something you can do, I'll let you help me. I'm going to mimeograph books."

"Does that mean writing out characters? That's no good. I suppose the books will be difficult."

"No, they won't be. It'll be short stories and novels. I'll show you later on." Jukichi suddenly burst out into a loud laugh.

"Ahh—you got me in the face." Not understanding what was so funny, O-Chiyo rubbed her cheek with her palm.

After making the rounds following up help-wanted ads in the papers, Jukichi had resolved to inure himself to work as a copyist for one yen, fifty sen a day. According to the employer, the mimeographed material was distributed to a limited membership and so there was no fear of arrest. In the unlikely event of any trouble, the nominal head of the society would bear responsibility. The copyists and suchlike had nothing to worry about.

O-Chiyo, who'd been smilingly leaning back against

Jukichi's knee, sat up. "Even that, if it goes well, will give me peace of mind. It'll be half like a game, won't it?"

"That's what I thought, so I took the job. But one yen, fifty sen a day is slave wages."

"It really is. One yen and fifty sen—it's what a house-keeper gets."

"That's right. The same as you used to earn in the old days. But it's better for a woman. Because occasionally you make some special income."

"What a mean thing to say. There's no call to say such a thing, even to me. You were bad that time. It's too much, to say that kind of thing now."

"O-Chiyo, if I were to get sick . . . would you go to work for me? Would you become a waitress, even . . . ?"

Putting his arm around her shoulder as she leaned up against him coquettishly, Jukichi peered down into O-Chiyo's face. Actually, thinking that she would broach the matter of her own accord, he had been waiting for her to do so. There having been absolutely no sign of that, however, he'd decided not to let this evening's opportunity slip by. He would introduce the subject point-blank and ask the woman how she felt about it.

"Yes, I could do that."

"Do you really mean it?"

"Yes. If you told me to, I would."

O-Chiyo's reply being slightly vague in its very explicitness, Jukichi tried to make sure of her. For her part, O-Chiyo had always lightheartedly thought that if it was something Jukichi told her to do, she would try to do it, no matter what. This did not particularly arise from a resolution that she would begrudge no sacrifice for Jukichi's sake. In short, it was O-Chiyo's nature to act in everything according to the situation, blindly and without reflection. When, in her days as a temporary house-keeper, she had been inveigled by the man into sleeping with him, she had done his will as if it couldn't be helped. When she had been proposed to by a respectable man, she had married him. But what she could not endure was to be held to account by those around her, to be treated in a systematic manner, according to the rules. It was why she'd been unable to be a wife in a household populated by in-laws. It was why, without thinking it humiliating or immoral, she had gone twice to the man's house in Kobinata-suidocho, just as she'd been asked. Her immediate acquiescence in Jukichi's suggestion that she become a waitress was the same sort of thing. Unable to think of any particular reason for refusing, she had simply assented. She didn't consider at all whether work as a waitress was suitable for her or not. To think things out ahead of time and then to act consistently on her decision were impossible feats for O-Chiyo.

The next day, O-Chiyo had Jukichi look at the advertisements in the newspaper and then went to the cafe district around the Ginza. At the first place, she was told that she was slightly overage and was turned down. At the next place, not only did she feel intimidated by a mob of thirty or forty applicants but, watching the large number of waitresses busily going back and forth, she realized for the first time what conditions were like in a cafe and began to think that she could never do the job. Before too long, her turn came and she was called into the office. A man of twenty-four or -five, his hair gleaming with brilliantine, meticulously questioned her as to her residence, full name, age, and personal history. After inquiring into her job record, he told her that she would be notified later on as to the results of the interview. Much relieved, O-Chiyo made her escape.

She waited three or four days, but no word came. Since Jukichi had said that she should not be shy but just go in and ask wherever she saw a help-wanted ad in the window, O-Chiyo once more set out for the Ginza. However, there were no such ads in the windows of the cafes along the main thoroughfares. Walking around wherever her feet led her, O-Chiyo was rather tired by the time she emerged into a back street, at the end of which could be glimpsed the avenue along the river by Kyobashi Bridge. Both sides of the street were lined with cafes. Here she finally spotted a help-wanted sign.

In the narrow entryway, beneath a glass-bead curtain, two pairs of high-heeled legs were visible. O-Chiyo, thinking it was one of those cafes where you had to wear foreign clothes, hesitated. Just then, a woman in Japanese clothes, her mouth full and working, abruptly stuck out her big face dusted with yellowish-brown makeup and tossed a banana skin onto the sidewalk at O-Chiyo's feet. Their eyes met. O-Chiyo, taking advantage of this opportunity, bowed. "Pardon me, but are you hiring waitresses?"

"Yes. Come right in. The boss is here." So saying, the woman pushed back with her fingertips the chewed-up, mushy banana that had oozed from her mouth.

Shouldering her way through the glass-bead curtain, O-Chiyo found herself in a single dirt-floored room that was so dark she could hardly see people's faces. In the far corner, beyond a clutter of tables and potted plants, a light over the bar illuminated bottles of Western liquors lined up on shelves and the faces of two men, one in a white kimono, the other in a dark business suit. Stumbling, O-Chiyo made her way toward them. With a bow, she began: "There was a help-wanted sign outside . . ." Breaking off his conversation, the man in the suit immediately asked her for her name and address. O-Chiyo, thinking that here too she would be told that they would notify her later, adjusting the shawl in her hand, said: "I'll wait to hear from you, then." The man casually replied: "You can start now. Pick it up as you go along."

"Oh. I'll do that, then."

Calling over a woman who seemed to be the head waitress, the man introduced them. The waitress, leading O-Chiyo into a three-mat room behind the bar, made her remove her shawl and haori.

"Our group is red. Today the second floor is red, so we'll go upstairs."

When, presently, it grew dark outside, although lights were turned on, the second floor seemed even more crepuscular than downstairs. Amid the constant playing of a phonograph, and accompanied by a voice calling out "Customers!," two men, surrounded by three or four waitresses, came up the stairs as if being dragged up them. Although none of them were drunk, waitresses and customers alike dumped themselves in a corner booth as if unable to remain on their feet. The six or seven upstairs waitresses immediately clustered around the group. One of them, bringing two or three bottles of beer, said as if reproaching the customers: "It's all right. It's the first sale of the day, so they're cheap."

"Before we drink, show us one of your tricks," one of the men growled. "Unless I drink something, I can't get in the mood," the waitress chided him.

Three of the waitresses, O-Chiyo among them, stayed in the booth a while. One of the guests, lifting onto his knees a waitress who was wearing Western clothes, put his hand up the kimono sleeve of another waitress. At this, the other guest abruptly pulled O-Chiyo to him and started to slip his hand up her sleeve.

"What the hell—this one. She's really on her guard, the bitch." The man pushed O-Chiyo away.

O-Chiyo, unaware that the women of this shop all wore their clothes next to the skin, did not know what the matter was. The waitress in Western dress, coming around to the side of the customer, said: "This person just started work today. Don't be too hard on her." With these words, she hoisted up her short skirt and straddled the man's lap. Two or three more bottles of beer had been brought to the table.

By now it was midnight. Afraid that she would miss the last trolley, O-Chiyo left by herself although the cafe hadn't yet closed. When she got back, Jukichi, still up, was at his desk copying out a story to be mimeographed. They began talking about today.

"Is that so. You certainly picked an awful place. But there can't be many like that. You've got to be patient and keep looking."

"Yes. That's all I can do. The good cafes on the main thoroughfares won't hire me, and all of the cafes require suitable dress. That's my main problem right now. The clothes at the pawnshop are all Taneko-san's. No matter how gorgeous they are, they aren't any use."

"Hm. They would be rather flashy for the Ginza. Well, why don't you start looking in some other section and work your way up to the Ginza?"

"That's really all I can do. I've already become too lazy to work as a housekeeper. Cafes after all are the places where the money's to be made."

The next day, as she had the day before, O-Chiyo set out to look for work as a waitress. Today, however, since she had no particular place in mind, it seemed like a hopeless search. Not only that, but from the little she had seen of the inside of the cafes as she'd walked around the back streets of the Ginza, O-Chiyo had already lost the desire to be a waitress. But for the time being, she had no other prospects and no one from whom to seek advice. As she went on her way, O-Chiyo remembered the old woman she'd gotten to know at the bathhouse. Although she'd gone as far as the trolley stop, she abruptly turned around and came back.

When she had heard O-Chiyo's story, the old woman said: "Well, then, ma'am, why don't you do this." Telling Jukichi that she was on trial service for three or four days at this or that restaurant, O-Chiyo was to pass the time at the old woman's house.

Since there was a telephone in the house, the old woman didn't keep a maid for fear of her secret leaking out. Occasionally, she would order food from a restaurant over the phone. Once or twice a month, the old woman would call in a temporary housekeeper and have her do the housework. Consequently, the kitchen sink and cupboards, rather than the uncared-for look of a large, poor household, had a neat and pretty appearance. Generally, men came calling from the afternoon into the evening. Summoning one of her girls by telephone, the old woman would show the guest up to the second floor. If there were two or three customers, having previously arranged it with the young woman, she would have the man go directly to an assignation house or inn that she did business with. Regular customers, knowing her circumspect way of handling things, got in touch with her only by telephone, going to a place of their own choice. For these reasons, there was no very conspicuous stream of callers at the house.

O-Chiyo, spending her days at the old woman's house from noon to evening, in the end saw all there was to see of the old woman's operations. For her part, the old woman, by showing her how everything worked in the house, meant to silently instruct O-Chiyo. Although thinking, on her way home, that it would be better not to spend too much time in such a place, O-Chiyo disliked trudging about looking for work as a waitress. And there was noplace else to go. So she would go back the next day and pass the time there. Taking a day off and then coming two or three days in a row, she became unable to stay away from the old woman's house. Sometimes, if several customers came at once, she helped the old woman out by making phonecalls. She was also left in charge of the house in the old woman's absence. Since not even Jukichi would believe that she was doing nothing but going around working as an apprentice waitress, she had the old woman call up a bar she did business with, inventing a story that she worked there. This meant she had to stay at the old woman's house from evening until midnight. She had to show Jukichi the tips that she had supposedly accumulated. One evening, despite the fact that a customer was waiting upstairs, the woman who was supposed to come, for whatever reason, did not come. It was already nearly eleven o'clock. There was no way a substitute could suddenly be summoned at this hour. Unable to bear the sight of the old woman's distress, at her prayerful entreaty O-Chiyo ascended the stairs to the second floor. She couldn't bring herself to say that if she gave in once there would be troublesome consequences. Two or three days later, that night's customer came back again. When he said that he must have the same woman as before, it was all the more difficult to refuse. And so, night by night, O-Chiyo descended further into the depths. However, she was able not only to pay off the interest at the pawnshop, but to pay in full that month's back rent.

EIGHT

O-Chiyo had not really considered what would happen if Jukichi found out about her secret. She hadn't
even thought much about whether her secret could be
preserved like this indefinitely. She merely hoped that it
would continue not to be known. She did not have the
time to think of a method to preserve it, or of what to
do should it be revealed. Or rather, she didn't have the
ability to think of such things. Perhaps, after Jukichi had
found out and given her a beating, they would talk about
a separation. But that would have no particular effect on
O-Chiyo's situation. Her road in life would not change
if she separated from Jukichi, nor, if they came together
again, would Jukichi's joblessness go away. If it could
somehow remain a secret until Jukichi found a regular
job . . . such was O-Chiyo's vague prayer.

Toward the end of that year, the cold was less severe
than usual. It was two or three days before New Year's
Eve. About half-past midnight, her usual time, O-Chiyo
came back, ostensibly from the bar, actually by cab from
Karasu-mori, where she had gone from the old woman's
house. Undoing the belt of her overcoat, she went upstairs and found Jukichi, who seemed himself to have just
gotten back. His hat and Inverness cape had been hung up,
but without having taken off his scarf he was squatting at
the brazier and blowing on the half-extinguished coals.

"The Ginza was so crowded you couldn't walk on it."

"It's the Year End Festival."

"The cafes there have stayed open until two o'clock since the twenty-fifth. They're even cheaper than Kanda."

"Well, they're in the right location." As she said this, O–Chiyo realized for the first time that the cafes in Kanda might also be open until two. To divert the conversation, she pulled out a foot warmer that had been put to one side and began to stir up the coals in the brazier. Jukichi took out his wallet.

"O–Chiyo, tonight I did something really dangerous. Of course, it was just by chance."

O–Chiyo looked worriedly at Jukichi.

"I'd heard there were 'escort girls' on the Ginza. I was tailing one of them and was just about to turn off into an alley, when I was accosted by a man in a cape. He wanted to go to some place where it was dark and buy some post-cards. Actually, I just happened to have some good ones on me. Recently, I've been carrying them around with the mimeographs. I suddenly felt like doing business. After all, the Ginza is the Ginza. I made two yen." Jukichi held up the silver coins.

Rather than being surprised, O–Chiyo thought of her own secret. She was at a loss for a good answer.

"It would be risky if I went to the same place every night. If I just do it every once in a while, as I'm taking a walk, it'll be all right."

"But it's dangerous. Unless you're extremely care-ful . . ."

"That's why it's an adventure. When you think about it, it's like a game. It's interesting. It's like being a pick-pocket or a shoplifter. Not that I'm a pickpocket or a shoplifter, of course, but shady, secret things are interest-ing. They're curiously entertaining, somehow. No matter how hard up I was, I could never be a respectable person."

O-Chiyo, feeling as if her secret was already known, thought it might be better to confess everything now. But she did not know how to begin. Lowering the earthen teapot, she started to stir up the coals again, which had begun to burn brighter.

"Why don't we buy something to eat with this money? The shops are probably still open tonight. If we go as far as the Slope, we can have some noodles. Don't you want something? Are you tired?"

"No . . ."

"Let's go out, then. It's awfully warm this winter, isn't it? Maybe we're in for another earthquake."

"Yes. There was a sudden shower yesterday evening."

Although fearful that he was enticing her outside with something in mind, preparing herself for it, O-Chiyo went out with Jukichi.

A soft wind had begun to blow, and a light mist had descended over the city. The pale, hazy aspect of the quiet late-night streets, wherever one looked, was like a summer dawn. Even the thinly veiled light of the stars did not seem at all like winter. Although all the shops were closed, the still flowing crowds of promenaders grew ever more lively as Jukichi and O-Chiyo neared Ushigome-mitsuke. Strolling ahead of them was a similar couple. From their conversation, the words "early shift" and "late shift" could be heard. Jukichi, as if remembering something, said: "O-Chiyo, what does your place do on New Year's? Are you off that day?"

"I haven't asked yet."

"They should give you three days off. You've earned it. It's already three months since you started working at that bar. They haven't given you a day off yet."

Once again, O-Chiyo was at a loss for an answer. Why,

just tonight, was Jukichi asking difficult questions? She even had the feeling that he knew and was pretending not to know, that by embarrassing her he was taking what revenge he could for her misbehavior.

"Something has come up. I've got to go home just this once. I was thinking of leaving tomorrow." O-Chiyo spoke quietly.

"Home? You mean Funabori?"

"Yes. Since Mother died, I haven't gone back even once."

"O-Chiyo. You probably don't mean to come back. If that's the case, please say so." Jukichi's voice had risen. Then, noticing the couple up ahead, he stopped. A voice said: "Is somebody there?" There was a sound of what seemed to be a kiss.

"But, I . . ." O-Chiyo began, dragging her feet. Her voice was almost inaudible. "It's because I've done something unforgivable . . ."

"Are you saying you want to separate?"

"But you probably won't forgive me."

"If I hadn't forgiven you, I wouldn't have kept silent up to now. O-Chiyo, it's all my . . . well, it's all on account of me that you . . . It can't be helped."

". . . . . . ."

"Before long I'll find a way of making a living. O-Chiyo, I've trusted you, so please stick it out a little longer. I beg of you."

Passing his arm around her from behind, he quietly drew her to him. O-Chiyo pressed herself to him.

"I . . . so long as you forgive me. But you must have thought I was a terribly brazen woman. That's so, and yet . . ."

"It's all right now. I understand. As long as you tell me everything I won't think badly of it."

"Really?" O-Chiyo, laying her head on Jukichi's shoulder, looked up into his face. Caught off balance by her weight, Jukichi steadied himself. Holding her tight, he went on: "As long as you feel the same about me, I won't think badly of you. For a long time I've thought there was something strange. But I couldn't bring myself to mention it. And I thought that you never would. So I kept silent. You must have been racking your brains."

The nearest person of the couple ahead of them, apparently catching the sound of their voices, dropped back a step or two and turned around. Then, evidently reassured that it was the same kind of couple as they were, the figure once more drew close to its companion and walked on. O-Chiyo, watching the couple recede into the mist, answered: "Yes, I was worried about it. But how did you come to understand?"

"How, you say. I understood, that's all. Although you told me you were working at a bar, you didn't come back drunk even once. Even your clothes never smelt of liquor. And your *tabi* socks were never dirty. That's why I thought it couldn't be a bar or cafe."

"That's just how it was."

"And it wasn't only that. There were other ways in which I understood." Once again drawing O-Chiyo close to him, walking two or three steps in silence, Jukichi added: "I can't really talk about it. In this kind of place . . ."

"What? Tell me."

"It would be too insulting."

"I don't care. Tell me, tell me." With a deliberately coaxing manner, as if making a joke of it, O-Chiyo opened her eyes wide and gazed up into Jukichi's face. Her expression, in the slanting light from the streetlamp, seemed to Jukichi especially captivating and winsome.

Stopping, Jukichi started to kiss O-Chiyo on the forehead as she looked up at him. But then, startled by a car's headlights that suddenly flashed upon them from behind, shielding the woman, he stood to one side. Glancing up ahead, he saw that the other couple had also stood aside. A train went by in the distance. Through the shadowy mist, electric advertising signs atop the roofs of houses on the far side of the Moat were visible behind the trees.

At a nighttime stall along the Moat, the two shared a cup of sake, something they had never done before. Oblivious of the late-night chill that with the rising wind had at last grown intense, they leisurely made their way back. From that night, in the flesh and in their hearts, the two became more and more inseparable.

Having had the experience of living with a willful, immoral older woman, Jukichi knew how to manage women by submitting to them. What would have been impossible for anyone with ordinary self-respect had by now become second nature with him. In Jukichi's eyes, the lives of respectable people seemed absurdly constricted and somehow hypocritical. By contrast, a lewd, indolent existence such as his seemed the happiness of life without its pretenses. His life with O-Chiyo, which had gone on for four or five years now, had at some point or other fallen into monotony. From that night, however, it suddenly picked up a peculiar liveliness. The thought that his woman was occasionally intimate with other men gave rise to various fantasies and violently aroused Jukichi's sexual desires.

As for O-Chiyo, knowing that she had her husband's

open permission not only removed any shame from her heart but, since she was working for Jukichi's sake, any feelings of shyness. She even felt proud somewhere in herself. And from her girlhood, O-Chiyo had taken a simple pleasure in the fact that she was attractive to all sorts of men. When she lived in Funabori, she'd been made much of by the young men of the neighborhood. When she went into service as a maid in a mansion, she'd been teased by the amorous houseboys. When she worked as a temporary housekeeper, she'd had advances made to her by the heads of several households. O-Chiyo did not think of this as humiliation, but as proof that she possessed something that men liked. This something, as time went by and the number of men she'd been intimate with increased, gradually became clearer to her. In her heart of hearts, she felt more and more triumphant. She was loved by Jukichi. And, in the same way, she must be loved by the other men, she thought, in her extreme simplicity. And so, as if she'd forgotten that she would turn thirty-three with the New Year, she was able to live lightheartedly, from day to day.

NINE

THAT day, by the time Jukichi got back after making a withdrawal from their postal savings account in Azabu-Tanimachi, O-Chiyo had gone out to work. The evening deepened into night, but she did not come back. It wasn't unusual for her to stay out overnight, so Jukichi did not particularly worry about her. As he always did on such frequent nights of sleeping alone, he took the opportunity to rest up from his habitual fatigue. He slept insatiably. The next day, however, even as the evening drew on, O-Chiyo still did not return, nor was there a phonecall. Thinking there might have been a mishap, Jukichi began to worry a little.

Reheating the remnants of the midday meal, with seasoned and fried miso and baked laver on the side, Jukichi had a solitary supper. Afterward he telephoned the Yoshizawa Inn, which had summoned O-Chiyo the afternoon of the previous day. He learned that she had been there until the evening. Her whereabouts after that was a mystery. Jukichi then called up two or three assignation houses that O-Chiyo used, but learned nothing further. Increasingly worried, Jukichi could only think of calling up some of her friends and companions in the trade, but he didn't know their telephone numbers. Thinking there must be something written down in a drawer of her mirror-stand or somewhere, he rummaged about but found nothing. . . .

"Nakajima-san, you have a caller." Just then, the voice of the glass-dealer's wife called to him from downstairs.

Descending three or four steps of the ladder-stairs, Jukichi peered around below him. His caller was Tamako, the girl he'd met yesterday on a street corner in Tame-ike.

"Please come up."

"Is Chiyoko in?"

"She's out right now. There's something I'd like to talk about, though. Please, come up."

Briefly exchanging civilities with the family of the glass dealer, Tamako followed Jukichi up the ladder-stairs.

"I'm sorry about yesterday."

"I thought you'd come to the house after that and waited for you. Did you take the room?"

"The one in Tame-ike, you mean? Actually I did, but then they said the downstairs tenant worked for a newspaper, so I gave it up. Today, I've been walking around searching all day, but there aren't many rooms where you have the use of a telephone."

"If you're in this neighborhood, they'll let you use the telephone here. I'll come and tell you when you have a call."

"I'll do that, then. I've already decided on it. Is Chiyoko-san still not back yet?"

"Actually, she went out at noon yesterday, and that's the last I've seen of her. I'm worried that she might have had a mishap. I've tried calling most of the places that have a telephone, but she wasn't at any of them. I even called up old woman Araki from when she was staying in Iida-machi, but I couldn't reach her at all. Because now she's in Yotsuya. I was just thinking of going there."

Tamako, because she hadn't worked out of the old woman's house in a long while and wanted her to arrange for a new base of operations, said she would go with Jukichi.

Turning left from the banks of the Moat in Honmura-cho, they wound their way through this or that dusky back street lined with little houses. Jukichi had only come here two or three times, so that once out of sight of the mailbox which had served him as a guide, they were lost. Not finding a drink shop or tobacconist's where he could ask the way, they wandered about until they came out midway on the Tsu no Kami Slope. Surprised, they retraced their steps, peering at the numbers on nameplates under the house eaves and on the gates by the dim light of streetlamps. Finally they found their way to the house they were looking for.

When Jukichi opened the wicket gate, the bell attached to it rang out merrily. But it was pitch dark behind the lattice door of the entryway. Although he called out two or three times, no one came. Just then, the telephone began ringing inside the house, but there was no sound of anyone's voice. The phone went on ringing for some little time, then suddenly fell silent. Only then did Jukichi and Tamako hear the voice of someone moaning in agony from the back of the house. They exchanged looks.

"The old woman's sick. Maybe she's all alone."

"She's rich. Probably she's been murdered."

"Oh, how awful. Don't frighten me." Tamako clung to Jukichi.

"I'll go in and take a look." Despite these brave words, Jukichi, with a sense of something uncanny, stood rooted to the ground in the entryway. Then, furtively reaching out his hand, he slid open the paper door an inch or two. There didn't seem to be a single light on in the house. The moaning voice, much more clearly audible now, seemed to be emanating from somewhere near the kitchen.

"Somehow I can't go in by myself. Tama-chan, go around to the back. She really should keep a maid in the house."

"What if I went next door and had someone come over? I don't like this at all." As Tamako spoke, the moaning voice grew even more intense. Involuntarily, Tamako bolted outside, followed closely by Jukichi.

"Even if you went around the neighborhood—I don't think she has much to do with the neighbors. We'll decide what to do after I take a look and see if she's sick or what."

Going around back to the kitchen, Jukichi fearfully slid open the glass door. By the light of a bulb that was on somewhere in the house, he could make out the figure of the old woman, her white hair in disarray, face down by the sliding paper doors between the wooden floor of the kitchen and a sort of tea room. Staying outside, sticking just his face inside the glass door, Jukichi called: "Auntie, Auntie Araki. Are you all right?"

The old woman simply moaned. Evidently she was in serious condition, almost unconscious. Somewhat reassured, however, by the tidy appearance of the kitchen and by the fact that there didn't seem to be blood anywhere, Jukichi came inside as far as the sink drain. Leaning over the movable floorboard, he called out again: "Auntie, Auntie Araki."

His repeated loud calls seemed finally to get through to the old woman. Clutching the paper door, she tried to raise herself. Seeing her face, Jukichi uttered an involuntary exclamation. Tamako, who'd been standing outside, now fled for dear life, stumbling over things until she was past the wicket gate. The old woman's face was swollen to about twice its normal size. Her eyes and nose seemed to have vanished. There was only the mouth, twisted to one side. At his first glimpse of this horrific visage, back-lit by the light bulb through the translucent paper door, Jukichi thought he was seeing a goblin.

Tamako came back, bringing a neighbor with her.

Presently, a doctor from the neighborhood arrived. According to his diagnosis, the old woman was suffering from something called periodontitis and would require oral surgery. Jukichi, accompanied by Tamako, went to the main thoroughfare of Yotsuya to look for a dentist. When they finally located one and brought him back, his diagnosis was even more pessimistic. The dentist in attendance, they took the patient to Keio University Hospital.

According to the doctor, if the poison that was rotting her jawbone attacked the old woman's brain, there was nothing to be done. It was past ten o'clock that evening when Jukichi and Tamako left the hospital.

"Tama-chan. Tonight certainly has been a strange night. Auntie Araki's a goner."

"You may be right. The way she looked . . ."

"Something may have happened to O-Chiyo, too."

Having the taxi they'd hailed along the way stop in front of the glass dealer's, Jukichi ran upstairs from the back entrance. Sliding open the paper door, he saw bedding laid out in the middle of the room. There, lying in bed with her back to him, was O-Chiyo. Both Jukichi and Tamako behind him, thinking she'd been in a car accident or the like, inadvertently cried out.

"O-Chiyo, what happened?"

Awakened by their voices, O-Chiyo murmured drowsily: "You're back."

"What happened to you?" Jukichi stood where he was in the doorway.

"Chiyoko-san. It's been a long time . . ." Tamako said, from behind Jukichi.

"Oh—it's Tama-chan. You're together . . ." O-Chiyo, with a strange look of her own now, started to get up.

"Didn't something happen to you?"

"What do you mean, didn't something happen?" More and more suspicious of Jukichi's demeanor, O-Chiyo widened her eyes.

"That's good, then. You're all right." As if noticing it for the first time, Tamako began to take off her coat.

"Well, this *is* odd."

"It's not odd at all. We were very worried about you. You've been gone since yesterday afternoon and didn't even call."

"Oh? I asked the maid to call. She must have forgotten about it. I'm sorry."

"We've been out to Auntie Araki's. It looks as if she's going to die."

"I was really frightened. Her face was like this." Mimicking the old woman's expression, Tamako gave a detailed account.

"There's never been a stranger night than tonight. We were worried, thinking you'd been hurt, and then when we went to Auntie Araki's, she was moaning away at death's door. . . ." As if exhausted, Jukichi sank down to the mat on his side.

"Strange, indeed. I had a lot of trouble myself last night. Something ridiculous happened. Even if I'd tried to, I couldn't have done something so ridiculous."

"What was it? We can't tell if you just smile to yourself like that."

"But when I think about it, it's just too silly. I can't talk about it. I picked up the wrong customer. Even I thought it was stupid of me. I was flabbergasted at myself."

"Chiyoko-san, that's awful."

"It happened on the spur of the moment. There was nothing I could do. I was on my way back from the Yoshi-zawa, when I ran into a customer under the Shinbashi

Bridge. He invited me to a meal, so I went with him to a noodle shop behind the Ginza. I thought he would take me to a department store and buy me something. We wandered around the Ginza for a while. It was the height of the evening promenade just then. In front of places like the Matsuya, you couldn't walk without being shoved and bumped. I was standing looking at the dolls in a window display, when a completely drunken student made as if he were going to purposely crash into me, so I stepped back. The man was two or three steps ahead of me by now. He'd stopped at a nighttime stall, so I stopped too. There were swarms of people, and I couldn't see a thing. I tried to slowly make my way through, but someone kept pushing me from behind. When I turned around, there was my customer walking away from me, I thought. I hurried after him and grabbed his hand, but then we got separated. I clung to him, got separated again . . . About thirty feet farther on, the crowd thinned out a little. I clung to him again, and said: 'You.' Then, when I looked at him from the side, it was somebody else. From behind, he had the same hat, the same Inverness cape, he was the same height, but he was the wrong person. I was so embarrassed I couldn't even say 'excuse me.' I just turned bright red and bowed. And then, the man smiled at me and took my hand. 'I'm already tired of walking. Let's take a cab,' he said. He hailed a one-yen taxi that was at the curbside. He was going to put me in that cab just as if I was his own woman. The driver had opened the door and was waiting. The sidewalk was jammed, and it seemed no time to stand around and argue. So I got into the cab with him. The driver said he'd go as far as Hama-cho for fifty sen. The man put his lips to my ear and whispered: 'Do you cruise the Ginza every night?' He thought I was one of those 'escort girls.' There was no particular need for an apology, so I kept silent and did what he said."

"That was pretty quick-witted of you. What happened after that? I'm sure it's worth hearing," Jukichi said, smiling. Tamako, too, from the side, drawing O-Chiyo out, said: "Where did he take you?" Just then, the downstairs clock began to chime. Glancing at her wristwatch, Tamako exclaimed: "Oh dear. It's already twelve o'clock. I'll have to say good-bye."

"Why don't you stay overnight? I'd like to hear more about your loverboy."

"That's all there is. I've told you everything."

"Oh? So you've broken up for good?"

"Yes." Tamako was starting to say something else, when this time the telephone began to ring. O-Chiyo knew that phonecalls at this hour could only be for her or the waitress who rented the front half of the second floor. Hurrying downstairs, she came back up almost immediately.

"Tama-chan. I'm already exhausted tonight. If you feel like going out, could you take my place? If so, I'll tell them that. It's a teahouse over in the Tsukiji landfill district. It's a good place." O-Chiyo signaled some numbers with her fingers.

"Yes. All right." Tamako nodded. "Overnight?"

"Probably. And so, this." O-Chiyo again signaled with her fingers. When she'd done so, she went downstairs again to give the answer to the other party.

TEN

THE next morning, O-Chiyo, saying she would go see how the old woman was, set out for the hospital. Jukichi, with the intention of sleeping until noon, crawled back into bed. As he thought he was dozing off, he heard a woman's voice outside the paper door calling for O-Chiyo. Thinking it was Tamako, on her way back from last night's destination, he called out: "Come in. She's just gone to the hospital."

Turning over in bed toward the door as it slid open, he saw that it was not Tamako. It was a woman of thirty or so in an out-of-style Western hairdo, evidently a house-maid. Although he'd seen her before, Jukichi could not remember who she was. The woman stepped briskly up to his pillow. Standing over him, she abruptly announced: "Something terrible has happened."

"Ah, so. Thanks for coming to tell me."

Immediately guessing everything by her demeanor and tone of voice, Jukichi sprang out of bed and took down some clothing from the wall.

"Who was it . . . ?"

"It's the Yoshizawa. Just now they took the madam away. And another detective is standing guard at the front desk so O-Kimi-san can't get out. There's a list of tele-phone numbers in the desk. If they find those numbers, everybody's in trouble. I happened to be in the privy just then and was able to escape. But I don't have a cent on me. I can't even make a phonecall. I came here because not long ago I came as far as the front door with O-Chiyo on our way back from the Konpira Shrine. That's why I came to warn her."

"The telephone in this house isn't safe. Please use a pay phone. I'll loan you a yen." Jukichi fished some change out of his sleeve.

"I'll pay you back later."

"Whatever happens, call me back again." When he'd gone downstairs with the woman, Jukichi immediately put a call through to Keio University Hospital. He had O-Chiyo paged and, using circumlocutions, told her not to come back to the house. Going back upstairs, he quickly went through the drawers of the mirror-stand and suchlike to see if there were any letters or receipts. Dragging out a trunk, a wicker suitcase, and a valise from the wardrobe, he dashed downstairs and hailed two taxis. Coming back upstairs, he stuffed everything he could get into the trunk, the suitcase, and the valise, starting with the bedding. Telling the glass dealer the first story that came into his head and paying off the back rent, Jukichi left half the luggage at the baggage depository at Shinbashi Station. Then, boarding the taxi into which he'd loaded the bedding and the valise, he paid a call on a kitchenware dealer named Fujita in the Senzoku-machi section of Asakusa. The shop was on a newly opened thoroughfare that ran past the Shochiku Theater straight toward South Senju. This kitchenware dealer was the husband of O-Chiyo's younger sister. O-Chiyo, with the idea of making his place an emergency hideout, had previously introduced Jukichi to him.

After dropping off the bedding and the valise there, Jukichi at once set about looking for a room in the neighborhood. When he came back at noon, he met up with O-Chiyo for the first time that day.

About half an hour after she'd arrived, O-Chiyo told

him, Auntie Araki had drawn her last breath. At this juncture, however, there was no time for the pair to have a leisurely discussion about the departed person. As soon as they'd finished a takeout lunch of rice topped with fried fish, the two decided to fan out through the neighborhood in search of a room. When they returned that evening to the kitchenware dealer's, O-Chiyo had found a room over a rice-dealer's shop along an alley diagonally opposite the Otori Shrine. Jukichi had found one over a laundry up an alley lined mostly by residential shops, near a large temple called the Nichirin in the Shibazaki section of Asakusa. Although both shops had a telephone, there were two Korean chauffeurs living at the rice shop. At the laundry there was only a concubine. The two immediately set out for the laundry with their bedding and the valise.

"O-Chiyo, what are we going to do? I left behind the mirror-stand, the brazier, the table, and the tea shelf. I thought that before it got too late this evening, I'd go back and get them and see what the situation is."

"Call up first. Find out whether anyone from the police has come, or what . . ."

"If they haven't come by now, it's probably all right."

"Not necessarily. Last year when Tama-chan was taken in, it was two days after the raid that the summons came, she told me."

"Everybody's taken in at the same time. Didn't you tell me that you and O-Shun-san from Hattori were the only ones who weren't charged?"

"That was for taxes, so we had to go. But nobody likes to go to that sort of place. I'm going to change my name for a while."

"What name will you take?"

"Isn't any name all right? The first time I changed it, I chose Tachibana."

"Hm. You borrowed the family name of the late Taneko-san."

"It's already four or five years ago. Now that Auntie Araki's dead, no one's likely to remember my name from that time."

"Let's make it Tachibana, then. I'll tell the people downstairs. After that, I'll call up the house in Shiba." Borrowing the phone downstairs, Jukichi made inquiries about the situation at the glass dealer's, their place of residence until this morning. Somewhat relieved to hear that no one had come, the two left the laundry together.

Along one side of the alley ran the tin-roofed fence of the Nichirin Temple. Keeping their eyes on the glittering streetlights beyond, Jukichi and O-Chiyo headed for the noisy thoroughfares. Soon they emerged onto the avenue in front of the Shochiku. At the corner, a news vendor was ringing his bell. Fishing out a copper coin, Jukichi haggled the vendor down on copies of the *Evening News* and the *People's Evening Edition*.

"It happened this morning, so it may not be in the papers yet." Glancing through the *Evening News* as they walked along, Jukichi went on: "The Matsuoka in Nezu was raided. There's nothing about the Yoshizawa, although it was part of the same raid."

"Which girls got arrested?"

" 'Hongo District, Tomisaka Ward: Ota Tetsu. Otsuka, Tsuji Ward: Miyabara Ko. Akasaka District, Hikawa Ward: Yoshioka Tsuyu . . .' "

"They got Yoshioka-san too? You probably know her —not too tall, the one who wore Western clothes . . ."

"Hm. That one who stayed overnight when we were

in Tanimachi . . . ? There are a lot more names." Handing
the *Evening News* to O-Chiyo, Jukichi opened the *People's
Evening Edition*. Fearful of the eyes of passers-by, O-Chiyo
folded her newspaper.

"It's because only low-price girls work out of the
Matsuoka."

"Have you ever been there?"

"Two or three years ago. The quality of their clientele
has gone way down."

When they turned onto the main thoroughfare, both
sides were lined with nighttime stalls, and there was a
thick flow of pedestrians. Without further conversation,
Jukichi and O-Chiyo walked as far as Thunder Gate.

"What will you do? Do you have someplace to go?"

"Yes, I thought I'd go to Hama-machi. That man I told
you about last night, the one I met on the Ginza? The
one who thought I was an 'escort girl' and took me along
with him. I promised him I would come tonight."

"Is it safe right now?"

"It's a house on Hama-machi Park. Not one of our
regular houses. There's nothing to worry about. It's time
to make a fresh start. I don't want to go broke right at the
start of the month from moving expenses . . ."

The two hailed a one-yen taxi. On the way to Shiba-
Sakuragawa, Jukichi dropped O-Chiyo off near the Meiji
Theater.

Cutting across the broad avenue, O-Chiyo made her
way up a narrow alley that turned off toward the Hettsui
Embankment. Outside the fifth or sixth house, there was
a lantern inscribed with the name Fukakusa. As O-Chiyo
slid open the lattice door, a maid whose face she remembered came out. "There was a phonecall just now. He said

he was coming right away. He said if you got here ahead of him to please wait. He called on the telephone." Saying this, the maid showed O-Chiyo into the same room where she had spent the night before last.

 ELEVEN

TOGETHER with tea, the maid had left copies of the evening edition of the *News* and the *Miyako News*. First opening the *Miyako News*, O-Chiyo searched for an item on the Matsuoka and the Yoshizawa, but there was nothing. Then she looked at the *News*, but it had only war reports from Chin-chou and Tientsin, nothing for a woman to read. Remembering that there was an *Evening News* in the pocket of her overcoat, O-Chiyo silently perused the article in it so as not to miss a single line or word. Then she went down the list of names and addresses of the twelve or thirteen women who had been arrested. Suddenly, she saw the name Fukazawa Tomi (19). Tilting her head, she lightly closed her eyes and counted on her fingers.

Fukazawa was O-Chiyo's own family name. The name Tomi resembled Tami, the name of the illegitimate child that O-Chiyo had borne in her eighteenth year. Just one character was different. And when she counted back from the age of nineteen given in parentheses, it was the age of the child she'd given birth to in the summer of the second year of Taisho. Perhaps the Fukazawa Tomi (19) whose name was exposed in print was her child O-Tami. For no particular reason, O-Chiyo thought she was.

When separation talks had started up shortly after her marriage to the sundries dealer, she had sent O-Tami out for adoption, some fourteen or fifteen years ago. The girl had been taken in by the family of a female hairdresser. After that, however, there had been a complete break in communication. It wasn't likely that O-Chiyo would hear any news of her daughter's career. And yet, somehow, she had the feeling that the O-Tomi in the newspaper was her daughter O-Tami. When she thought that the girl was a social outcast like herself, rather than humiliation she felt only a desperate longing for her. Unbearably, she wanted to see her face, to talk with her. From the direction of the main thoroughfare, she could hear a newsboy calling out an extra, and from a house somewhere nearby there were lively voices. Leaning on her elbows on the tea table, plunged in vague thought, O-Chiyo presently heard the sound of footsteps of someone coming up the stairs and the maid's voice. Carefully, she folded up the *Evening News*.

"He's here." With the maid's voice, the paper door slid open. Laughing as if he'd begun to exert an effort, the customer of the night before last entered the room. "Have you been waiting long?" No sooner had he said this than, regardless of the maid looking on, he stuck out a thick, hairy arm from the folds of his Inverness cape and, pulling O-Chiyo to him, rubbed his cheek against hers. Evidently well past fifty, the man retained on his gleaming bald head only a white fringe above the ears and around the back. But he was broad-shouldered and powerfully built, and his oily red face, in which the lips and nose were particularly prominent, gleamed brilliantly like his pate. This old man, Sugimura by name, was the owner of a wool business and the proprietor of a magnificent building on the West Ginza. In any red-light district or cafe, there are always one or two legendary lechers who surface in the gossip of the ladies, but few could have fitted the mold as well at a single glance as this wool merchant. Over the past twenty or thirty years, he had thoroughly familiarized himself with all classes of prostitutes. As he grew older, he had become dissatisfied with ordinary methods of pleasure. He was always on the lookout for strange new incitements. Since that night on the Ginza, when he'd happened to have his sleeve plucked by O–Chiyo in the crowd, and had thought that this was one of the "escort girls" he'd heard about, he'd come to feel that he could satisfy all his habitual desires in one night with O–Chiyo.

"Is the bathwater heated yet?"

"Yes."

"Then warm up the room across the way. Light the stove. Please." Even as he spoke, Sugimura was undoing his obi, to the maid's consternation.

"I'll bring your nightclothes right now." Saying this, the maid fled into the corridor.

"I don't need such things." Sugimura clasped the diminutive O–Chiyo to his shaggy chest. "Let's get in the tub together. Eh?"

O–Chiyo, used to such behavior, without making any particular outcry of surprise, allowed herself to be taken off to the bath as the man said. The maid, following them with their yukatas, readied the little room across the way and lit the electric stove. Then, a few moments later, she slid open the door of the bath preparatory to ushering in another guest. The two were still talking in the bath. Surprised at such a long bath, and hushing her footsteps, the maid withdrew. These days, it was not only her own Jukichi who was nice to O–Chiyo. It was not unusual for some of her customers as well to treat her kindly. That was why, even when she met up with an ugly man and was subjected to his irrational antics, the experience was not entirely without interest for her. Repressing her feelings of disgust and outrage, she experienced the birth of a kind of thrilling pleasure, and at times even deliberately sought out such pleasure. Also, this evening, knowing that Sugimura had money, O-Chiyo meant to make a request for a tidy little sum. In order to gain his favor, she was of a mind to put up with just about anything. O-Chiyo wanted enough money to have the young woman whom she felt was her daughter released from detention. From experience, she knew that customers who patronized unlicensed prostitutes, no matter how nicely they treated them, seldom came back more than three times. Generally, it was only two times. If she was going to make her request, tonight was the right time.

O-Chiyo's scheme was successful beyond her anticipation. Sugimura, for all his playing around, was a man of extremely crude mentality who never doubted his own judgment. Observing O-Chiyo's complaisant attitude, he'd concluded that he would not easily find another woman like her, search as he might. Having arbitrarily decided that it was more than a spirit of business that had prompted O-Chiyo to pluck at his sleeve the night before last on the Ginza, he desired to make her his own for a while. His only worry was whether there was a man in the background. Even that, if the man would simply stay in the background, was no great problem. But if he came forward and even threatened Sugimura . . . Thinking it best to first sound out the woman before she knew his name or occupation, he said: "It's all right. If that's all you need, I'll make it a year's end present. I'll give it to you this evening. By the way, wouldn't you like me to take care of you? I'll set you up in a house. Won't you say yes? I'm not suggesting anything unreasonable. I wouldn't put any restraints on your freedom."

"Fine. If that's the way it is." O-Chiyo's answer did not sound overly enthusiastic.

"You agree, then? If that's so, the sooner the better. I'm the sort of person who once he thinks of something can't stand dawdling over it. Won't you start looking for a house right away? Tomorrow, even."

"Yes."

"Anywhere's all right. In Kyobashi or Nihonbashi would be the most convenient for me. You can telephone this house any time of the day or night. I'll rent the place for you as soon as you find it."

"Well, I'll start looking right away."

"Is your mother or somebody living with you?"

"Right now, we're not together."

"You don't have an older brother or an uncle? Ha ha ha. Not that it matters, that sort of thing."

"No, there's nobody. If there were, I wouldn't be in this sort of business."

"I trust you. Investigations of background are boring."

"Even though I seem this kind of person, I'm surprisingly honest. I won't make any trouble for you."

"That's why I said right off I trusted you. Are you going to stay the night again? How about it?"

"Either way is all right with me. But early tomorrow morning there's something I must do. I'm making a grave-visit. . . ."

As soon as the money was in her hand, O-Chiyo felt she could not wait another minute to find out news of the young woman she thought was her daughter. Luckily, toward midnight, there was a fire over toward the Ginza. Making hasty preparations, Sugimura took his leave.

TWELVE 〜

USUALLY at a loss, with nothing to do, after O–Chiyo had spoken to him that evening and they'd settled on a course of action, Jukichi suddenly had so much to do that he felt that even if he had two bodies it wouldn't be enough. His first task, so as to establish O–Chiyo as Old Baldy's concubine, was to quickly find a house, move out of the rented room they had only just moved into today, and also, at the same time, to find another rented room in the neighborhood of the concubine's house so he could keep an eye on things. Another task was to go to the police station where the old madam called Matsuoka and a large number of her employees were being detained and, after making sure that the Fukazawa girl was indeed O–Chiyo's daughter, to arrange for her release.

By reading the advertisements in the newspaper, it was easier than he thought to find a house for O–Chiyo. The other things were more difficult, and he made no immediate progress. When he went to the police station, the girl called Fukazawa had already been released. Although by calculating from the girl's permanent address he determined at least that she was O–Chiyo's love child, his suspicions were aroused by the fact that apparently her records had not been transferred to the register of her adoptive family. Now, as at the time of her birth, she seemed to be O–Chiyo's. Ascertaining her address at the time of her arrest, Jukichi tried to get in touch with the girl herself. However, he was told by her landlady that after her release she had cleared out, leaving no forwarding address. Waiting for the old madam Matsuoka to be released, he visited her establishment also, but again without success. Finally, he tried to find out the address of her adoptive family. But even that, with the passage of time, had become unknown.

That year seemed to end in even more hectic fashion than other years. O-Chiyo greeted the new year in a house in Hatchobori, Jukichi in a rented room in Shintomi-cho just two or three blocks away. Soon it was nearly February, but the whereabouts of the persons he was seeking remained a mystery.

Calculating the comings and goings of Sugimura, Jukichi spent his days and nights in O-Chiyo's house until the dangerous hour. At the sound of the front door sliding open, he was out the back door. Then, about midnight, he came back. If there was a flicker of light in the papered back windows of the second floor, this was a sign that Sugimura was staying for the night, and Jukichi would return to his rented room. The next day, he would peer through the latticework of the front door. If the potted lily atop the patten-box had been turned around backward, this was a sign that there were no visitors, and Jukichi could enter the house openly. If, however, that was not so, he would quietly continue on his way. Unlike the life of husband and wife living together to which he had long since grown accustomed, this life of an adulterer, exactly such as might appear in an Edo-period novel, provided Jukichi a new source of stimulus and interest.

One night, when Jukichi had thought it was already too late for Sugimura, there was the sudden sound of the lattice door sliding open. Surprised, Jukichi fled out the back. A cold wind was blowing. But the nighttime stalls had opened along Hatchobori Avenue, and there was a lively flow of passers-by. Aimlessly strolling along, Jukichi came to the Sakura Bridge. Across the canal, the lights of the Ginza in the distance lit up the entire sky. Continuing his stroll, Jukichi came to Kyobashi Bridge. From amid the swarming crowds and the streetlights, there was the sound of recorded military songs and the cries of newsboys hawking extras, now near, now far, as the wind brought them to the ear. It lent a harshness to the congested nighttime scene. As he crossed the bridge, rather than the news of the Shanghai Incident, Jukichi was thinking of the time when O-Chiyo had first plucked at the sleeve of the bald-headed Sugimura on the Ginza. After that, mulling over Sugimura's ugly face, and how, without particularly minding this, O-Chiyo welcomed his advances with pleasure, he thought there was nothing so strange as a woman's nature. These past months and years, from the acidulous gossip of her colleagues and the old madams, Jukichi had been well aware that O-Chiyo was much in demand among the customers, but that after all was hearsay. Not until now, after he'd begun to frequent the concubine's house, had he been able to clearly observe O-Chiyo in action after having gotten a good close look at her customer's face. And yet, Jukichi did not think her conduct either heartless or mortifying or shameful. Only, it gave him a heavy, depressed feeling to think about such things. Wandering through the night streets, he wanted only to observe the thickly made-up faces of the women sitting outside cafes, the legs of women revealed by their Western dresses, or, shadowing a couple walking hand in hand, to eavesdrop on their murmured conversation.

Turning off the darkened embankment into a back

street where there were few passers-by, Jukichi paused outside a pharmacy, his eye caught by its window display. Becoming aware that a woman had stopped not far from him, he turned around. It was the waitress, by name Ito Haruko, who had rented the room in front when he and O-Chiyo had been living on the second floor of the glass dealer's in Sakuragawa-cho.

"Ah, Nakajima-san. It's been a long time."

"Are you still living in the same place?"

"No. I've moved to a street behind the Kabuki Theater. Where are you?"

"Shintomi-cho."

"And Chiyoko-san? How is she?"

"Something has come up. She's living by herself now."

"Oh, really?"

"It's good to split up every once in a while."

"You taught me a lot back then."

"It was mutual."

"Nakajima-san, I have a request to make. I've run out of mimeographs."

"I don't have any right now, but I'll make some for you in two or three days."

"Please. I'm at the Carmen. It's on that back street where the Hattori Clock shop is."

"You mean in back of Owari-cho?" Jukichi could not understand what a waitress from a cafe in Owari-cho was doing around Kyobashi Bridge at nine o'clock at night.

"If you go from here, it's on the left. It's a small cafe, but you'll recognize it right away."

"Are you on your way there?"

"Business is bad, and I have to think of other ways to make money. When I'm off from the cafe, I'm out picking up customers. If things go on this way, there won't even be work at cafes."

"Ah, yes . . ." Jukichi, remembering what O-Chiyo had done the previous year, realized that there must be all sorts of women prowling the Ginza these days.

"Do you take them back to the cafe, or . . . ?"

"There are some real Lotharios among them."

Just then, a woman with her hair shingled and in Western dress, apparently a friend of Haruko's, came up. "Back there in that alley, a hobo was taking a leak. A bit much even for the Ginza. Ha-ha."

"You're in a good humor this evening, I see."

"In a word, it's a bit much even for the Ginza."

Jukichi, looking at the woman's face, recognized her. She was Yoshioka Tsuyu. When they'd been living two or three years ago in Azabu-Tanimachi, she had come to visit O-Chiyo and had stayed the night. And last year, she had been one of those whose names were bared in print by the *Evening News* in early December. Although recognizing Jukichi herself, in front of Haruko the woman said nothing, merely acknowledging the acquaintance with the expression of her eyes.

It occurred to Jukichi that this woman might know something about the Fukazawa girl from the previous year's incident.

"Is your cafe the Carmen? Together with Haruko . . . ?"

"Yes." Tsuyuko's reply was guarded. From the side, Haruko said: "This gentleman's name is Nakajima-san. Last year we lived on the same second floor."

"Oh, is that so? I'm Tsuyuko."

As they walked along, Jukichi, taking advantage of Haruko's being two or three steps ahead of them, drew closer to Tsuyuko. "Do you know a girl called Fukazawa Tomiko? From the raid on the Matsuoka . . ."

"Yes. I know her."

"Do you know where she is now?"

"I might."

Just then, Haruko called out to a passing group of drunken men.

"Hey there, loverboys. How about going somewhere for a cup of tea?"

Taking advantage of the interval, Jukichi gave Tsuyuko O-Chiyo's exact address.

O-Chiyo had given her daughter O-Tami for adoption by the hairdresser's family in Shinei-cho of Kyobashi Ward in the fall of the sixth year of Taisho, when late one night a tidal wave had pushed its way up the Sumida River, inundating Tsukiji and reaching as far as Kobiki-cho. O-Tami was five years old at the time.

A frequent customer at the hairdresser's shop was an ex-geisha of Yanagi-bashi, now a concubine. After seeing O-Tami being led by the hand by the hairdresser on festival days in the neighborhood, she took pity on the little girl. Whenever she went to such places as Asakusa on a shrine-visit, she always took O-Tami along and bought various things for her.

Two or three years later, the hairdresser, who had long been a widow, took a young husband. This adoptive husband did not like children and was prone to mistreat O-Tami. The concubine, whose patron's name was Tsukayama, took O-Tami into her own house and had her attend grade school. Meanwhile, the hairdresser, hot on the traces of her inconstant husband, vanished one night and was never seen again. With nowhere to go, O-Tami was brought up by the concubine and in effect became her daughter.

Shortly before O-Tami's graduation from grade school, a purse belonging to one of her classmates was stolen. Although there was no sure proof, O-Tami's demeanor was suspicious. A note was sent from the principal to the concubine. Taken aback, the concubine conferred with her patron about what to do with O-Tami. "It doesn't matter. Let her play around the house," the patron said.

This Tsukayama was the owner of an electrical appliance factory, which he had inherited from his father. However, foreseeing the labor agitation that would continually plague the business after the enforcement of universal suffrage, he quickly sold the factory. Distancing himself from the disorders of contemporary society, he passed his self-justified days in reading and collecting antiques.

In the year of the Tokyo Earthquake, O-Tami turned eleven. It was when she had just left the grade school and was taking sewing lessons. Although the concubine rented a house in Shibuya almost the minute she had emerged from the shelter in Hibiya Park, O-Tami, who had gone for her sewing lesson, never came back. Four years passed. Even in the spring of the second year of Showa, when the concubine lay fatally ill with erysipelas, there was still no word as to whether O-Tami was alive or dead.

The following spring, however, Tsukayama went with a geisha to Hakone. The old couple who were staying in the next room at the inn had with them a girl whose face strongly recalled that of the child O-Tami. When Tsukayama made inquiries, sure enough the girl was O-Tami, now sixteen years old.

The old couple, who had formerly been moneylenders in Hakozaki-cho, had rescued O-Tami on the day of the Earthquake as they fled helter-skelter through the city. Taking her with them to their hometown of Kiryu, they spent the rest of the year there. Since returning to Tokyo, while waiting for someone to come and claim her, they had brought up O-Tami as if she were their own child.

Tsukayama informed the old couple that since the concubine who had so loved O-Tami had died, there was no one to take her in. Promising the girl a gift of money and saying that he would take a part in talks about her future, he left the inn.

More than half a year later, Tsukayama had business that took him to Niigata. As he boarded the train, he once again chanced to meet the old moneylender and O-Tami. The old man said that shortly after their return from Hakone his aged wife had died. Taking along O-Tami so he would have someone to talk to, he was on his way to the hot springs at Ikaho. As he listened to the old man's story, Tsukayama idly observed O-Tami. In little more than six months, she had changed almost unrecognizably. She now seemed completely adult. Tsukayama was unable not to wonder at the transformation. Indefinably, in her figure and her looks, there was the precociously seductive aspect that is often seen in the apprentice geisha who conceals her young age.

Tsukayama, fantasizing variously about the relationship between the old moneylender, on the far side of sixty, and the sixteen- or seventeen-year-old O-Tami, thought he would like to find out the truth of the matter. However, there was no opportunity to. Another half-year or so went by. Then, unexpectedly, he received a letter from O-Tami.

O-Tami had become a dancer at a cafe. Her letter was an unabashed request for money.

For about two years after that, Tsukayama had no news

of O-Tami. Then, coming across an item in the *Evening News*, he learned of her arrest. Engaging a lawyer, he made arrangements for her release.

"I was afraid the girl was a kleptomaniac, but happily it seems not to be so. It would have been a nuisance if she'd become a thief or a shoplifter. This sort of thing, if it's her lot in life, is probably better. It's in the natural order of things that she go from apprentice geisha to geisha. It's her fate."

Having this sort of conversation with the lawyer, Tsukayama spoke smilingly.

Although he felt sympathy for O-Tami, who to all intents and purposes was an orphan, Tsukayama had no wish to come forward to admonish and instruct her. Rather, with a cool interest, he merely observed the progress of her eventful life from the outside. Both by temperament and philosophical outlook, Tsukayama felt an extreme pessimism toward human life. Rather than entering a respectable profession and either falling into dire poverty or else agitating herself with the pretensions of success, it was happiness for her to lead an ignorant, promiscuous life, like a bit of trash floating along in the gutter. Rather than moral intervention, Tsukayama thought, the best way of understanding O-Tami was to help her out with small amounts of money and to extricate her from the occasional disaster.

One day, Tsukayama received a letter from O-Tami. It was a long letter, like a short story.

I have met my true mother, whom I thought I would never meet in all my life. I thought it was my duty to tell you, so I am writing this letter. To explain how, and why, I met my true mother, I have to completely expose not just my secret, but my mother's and her lover's. That is why I can't tell this to anyone but you. My mother, from a long time back, has been living the same kind of life as myself. Most likely, at one time or another, my mother and I have even slept in the same house, but that was nothing we knew about. Without knowing she was my mother, I even heard stories any number of times from my friends about an older woman called Tachibana Chiyoko (Tachibana Chiyoko is my mother's professional name). And a friend of mine called Tsuyuko, two or three years ago when my mother was living in Tanimachi in Azabu, even stayed at her place one night because it was raining too hard to go back. For all that, we never had a chance to meet, and never had a chance to know each other. What a big place Tokyo is, I thought.

Two or three days ago, Tsuyuko-san came to visit me. "There's somebody who very much wants to meet you," she said. "Will you meet her?" Since we were fined by the police at the end of last year, Tsuyuko-san has been working at a bar in back of the Ginza called Carmen. Hearing Tsuyuko-san's story, I was surprised. When I learned that my true mother was a woman who did the same thing for a living as myself, I didn't feel sad about it. I felt—when I say "happy," it sounds strange, but somehow I felt a friendly, affectionate emotion. Maybe that was why, even when I remembered how my mother had never come to see me in all the long months and years since she gave me away to other people, I didn't feel any resentment at her heartlessness. Perhaps if my mother had been a fine, respectable lady, I would have hated her. I think, also, that if I had been ashamed of my station in life I could never have shown my face to my mother, no matter how much I wanted to see her. It seems that my mother, after all, felt the same way. The shame we both felt under the circumstances drew us close to each other.

I hurriedly set out for my mother's place in Hatcho-bori. Since I'd heard about my mother's hours from my friend Tsuyuko, I thought the afternoon would be the best time to call on her. I got there at about three. A girl of twelve or thirteen answered the door and went upstairs to get my mother. My mother came down. She seemed to have been asleep and was pulling together the front of her yukata.

"So. Please come in. It was very good of you to call."

My heart was full, and I didn't know what to say. Tongue-tied, I followed her into a sort of downstairs parlor or tea room. My mother, saying she would put something on over her yukata, went upstairs again and did not come down for the longest time. As I was thinking that perhaps one of her customers had come and I should call another time, there was a sound of footsteps on the stairs. I listened closely. It seemed to be not one person, but two. In a moment, the door slid open.

"My goodness—they didn't even give you a cushion to sit on." Seating herself on the other side of the brazier, my mother immediately started to make some tea. Unable even to say "It's been a long time," I tried to think of something appropriate.

"You're very busy," I finally said. It's something we often say in our profession, by way of a compliment. It later struck me how funny it was to say that kind of thing here. I don't know how my mother took it, but she didn't seem particularly offended.

"It's not a customer. It's someone I have to introduce to you."

"Is it your man, Mother?"

Just then, a man of about forty showed his face in the opening of the door.

"Welcome. I've been looking all over for you since the end of last year. When one doesn't know where somebody is, no amount of looking around will find them." Saying this, he sat down by my mother. Since I knew everything about him from my friend Tsuyuko, even his name, I didn't greet him formally.

"And I was practically next door. It's strange." I smiled.

"Were you with Tsuyuko-san all the while?" my mother's lover asked. With that, I told all about how I'd first become friends with Tsuyuko at a dance hall in Shinjuku and had rented a room with her, and after that how we were both arrested and had our dancer's licenses taken away and could not even appear at any dance hall inside the city limits, and then how, getting an introduction from the owner of a place in Gotanda, I'd switched to this kind of work.

My mother asked me if I was going to change my name, or think of some way to become a dancer again. Or wouldn't it be safer to be a waitress, like Tsuyuko? At first I'd liked being a dancer, but when it became nothing but a job it got rather boring. It was such hard work, and I didn't like being bound by the regular hours. I didn't want to be a dancer again. Even waitresses, if you worked at a place like Tsuyuko's, you had to go out into the street and grab people you'd never seen before, so if you thought of what might happen, it was really quite dangerous. I explained all this in detail.

In order to economize on my room rent, how would it be, my mother asked, if I were to move in with her. She planned to stay in this house a while longer until she had enough money saved, and then start up a teahouse for girls and their customers in some neighborhood where rents were low. Her lover chimed in from the side that they already had more than two thousand yen saved.

Up to now, I hadn't given a single thought to the future. When I heard that they had two thousand yen in savings, I blurted out: "You've really worked hard," and looked at my mother. My mother was eighteen when she had me, and so she was already thirty-seven. And yet her hair was still thick, she had a good figure, and the untidy way she wore her yukata she looked like a mature young woman of twenty-seven or -eight. When she goes out, I thought, she looks even younger. When I was at the dance hall, there were girls who had saved their money and were putting up houses for rent, but my mother looked even younger than them. According to everybody, these girls who had gone into the housing business were a little bit stupid and did whatever a man told them to. They never did anything but save money. I wondered if after all my mother were not that kind of person too. You can tell at a glance that she's not a bad person. She's pretty and looks young, but there's something weak about her. She never gossips about others or makes small talk. When this sort of person puts her mind to saving money, there's no stopping her.

I thought I'd like to ask my mother if she still knew the man who was my father, but the subject didn't come up that day. Besides, right from the start, I'd grown up without knowing there was such a person as my father. Having never heard anything about him, I didn't yearn all that much for my dearly beloved father. That was why, meeting my mother for the first time, I didn't want to force her to talk about him. Rather than a father whom I have never seen, the person that I long for is the old woman who brought me up in Funabori. I was only three or four when she died, so I don't even remember her face. But at night, when I am all alone in the pitch dark and I stare at one place, or on nights when I can't sleep and am tiredly half-dozing, sometimes I have the feeling that I can vaguely see that old woman and the countryside along a river. You might even call it a vision. If I am to say who is dear to me, it's my aunt who lived in Shinei-cho before the Earthquake, and yourself. As I've told you in a previous letter, the happiest time of my life was when I lived in the house in Shinei-cho. I will never forget how, taken by the hand by my aunt, I went for walks along the river in Akashi-cho and caught crabs. My two happiest memories are both of places where there was flowing water. And the two people whom I loved the best in my childhood both died.

I've decided to stay at my mother's place for a while. If anything comes up, I'll let you know. Until then, sayonara.

Tamiko

February 16, 1932

Library of Congress Cataloging-in-Publication Data

Nagai, Kafū, 1879–1959.
    [Tsuyu no atosaki. English]
    During the rains & Flowers in the shade : two
novellas / by Nagai Kafu ; translated by Lane
Dunlop.
        p.   cm.
    ISBN 0-8047-2259-5 :
    —ISBN 0-8047-2260-9 (pbk.) :
    1. Nagai, Kafū, 1879–1959—Translations into
English.   I. Nagai, Kafū, 1879–1959. Hikage no
hana. English. 1994.   II. Title.   III. Title: During
the rains.   IV. Title: Flowers in the shade.
V. Title: During the rains and Flowers in
the shade.
PL812.A4T7513   1994
895.6'342—dc20   93-24945
                                                            CIP